Published in Canada by ALGOTEXT INC.
33 Orlando Blvd., Scarborough, Ontario, M1R 3N5

National Library of Canada Cataloging-in-Publication Data

V. A. STEPHEN LENAGHAN, 1919 -
"SUPER MATH-E-MAGICS!!" . . . AMAZING MATH TUTOR
(The Joy of Learning High-Speed Calculating Strategies, Amazing Short Cuts and Acquiring an Intelligent Number Sense – a MATHTUTOR without using a Calculator!)
. . . by STEPHEN LENAGHAN.

Includes Short Cuts, Magic Squares, Index, Answers to Tests.
Training Tips for Stage Calculators: Mental Magic Acts, Pensa, etc.

This publication is expressly designed to engender "Number Sense" in the young and older persons who have enquiring minds, and dedicated to the students and/or others who are always on the lookout for something devious, and entertaining. For mentalists and conjurers, students searching for easier methods to be successful, and the like. It is not meant to replace math teachers, but to create diligent experimenters in mathematics without using a calculator.

ISBN 0-9697878-0-4 (paperback): $10.95 (Canada), $9.95 (U.S.), £6.50 (UK)

Lenaghan, Stephen V. A., 1919-
1. "SUPER MATH-E-MAGICS!!" "Be a Whiz MATH-E-MAGICIAN!" 2. Title.

Cover *"Hi & Lois"* – Cover Cartoon by permission of Toronto Star Syndicates, Toromto, Ont., Canada.
Book Chapter Cartoons by Dick Gibson, Canadian Newspaper Cartoonist, Brampton, Ontario, Canada.
Printed and OTA-bound, by Webcom Limited, Scarborough, Ont., Canada.
Cover finish: Webcom's exclusive ***Duracoat*** **.**

Algotext Publishing, 33 Orlando Boulevard
Scarborough, Ontario, Canada M1R 3N5 Fax : (416) 444-5044

First Edition, March, 1994
First mass market edition, Second Printing, September, 1994

9 8 7 6 5 4 3 2 1

recycled paper

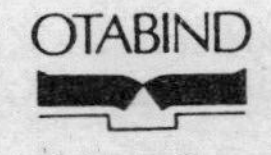

The pages in this book open easily and lie flat, a result of the Otabind bookbinding process. Otabind combines advanced adhesive technology and a free-floating cover to achieve books that last longer and are bound to stay open.

May we introduce MATHEW, our SUPER MATH CAT!
He's small, he's round, and he's so slightly fat.
He will tickle your fancy, and whisk up his tail;
You will want to ignore him, but to no avail.
He's your mentor, tormentor, and so that is that!

But get used to his prompts, his talents – he's witty;
He'll badger and hound you, (that's strange for a kitty);
He'll bewilder your mind with Short Cuts quite crazy;
That you'll dazzle your friends as "a kid that ain't lazy".
Now stick your nose in this book, and don't ask for pity!

Meet A Real Math Philanthropist!

WALTER H. ANNENBERG, American, Ambassador-retired, ex-Navy, etc., etc., "Who's Who in America" for several inches of financial connections, and a publishing mighty, has, in one generous action, with just a stroke of a pen, done more for his country than any single living person could do.

The media of North America have bestowed on him "the Laurel Tribute":

For giving the largest single gift ever made to public education in the United States. Through his Annenberg Foundation in St. Davids, Pa., the publishing tycoon has announced $500 million in matching grants over five years to help renovate school programs, especially to curb violence. "I'm deeply troubled by the violence in some grade schools and high schools," he said, "and if this continues, it'll not only erode the educational system but will destroy our way of life."

This Bulletin was released December 24, 1993, Toronto Star.

(When Ambassador Annenberg had the opportunity to review our book, SUPER MATH-E-MAGICS, in January, 1994, he "appreciated the opportunity to review your book . . . and thank you. We are all enjoying the various brain-teasers, and hope the book will find the widest circulation. We hope the math teachers' associations could be helpful.")

— GILLIAN NORRIS-SZANTO, Program Officer

Let's remember that an intelligent and working mind is an asset to future prosperity in one's lifetime. Brutality in schools must be eliminated once and for all time. Crime has no future! Think!

CONTENTS

INTRODUCTION – iii
PREFACE – iv

CHAPTER 1: Interested in a QuickTUTOR Look?
A review of memories past in the Land of Math! 50 Minute Wizards! Ho-Ho-Ho!

CHAPTER 2: What's the Basis of Arithmetic?
Short Cuts! Up-Some & Down-Some! Mental Aptitudes? Order of Operations

CHAPTER 3: Coming to Terms with MATH-E-MAGICS!
Rote Method gets a High Grade in Math Learning! Speed Reading, Music?

CHAPTER 4: Computing Mentally, Short Cuts
Strategies of Computing. Meet your Tables. Step up and get a Short Cut!
Square Short Cuts. So what's the difference, let's square it another way!

CHAPTER 5: TUTOR BOOM-E-RANGS
Complementary & Supplementary Multiplication
Speed and accuracy at your mind's level. Get on the Stage, Coach! Stage 1, 2, 3, 4.
Complex Complementary Multiplication, Supplementary Multiplication, and
wonder of wonders, Half Complementary Multiplication! Boy is this Math *Weird*!

CHAPTER 6: Magic Squares
What can you say about Magic Squares except they're Magic!

CHAPTER 7: "The Mind Boggler!"
You've heard of Musical Chairs, here's Tables doin' the same thing!
Your head will spin! What's all this hullaballoo about NUMBER SENSE!?

CHAPTER 8: What's a Prime Number?
When I was young and in my Prime! Oddities if you can find them!
Some primes are random and others fall through some guy's Sieve!

CHAPTER 9: Big Time Spender . . . Number 7!
7 is so Prime he's special, but very odd! So is 142857143, a queer number!

CHAPTER 10: "Here's PENSA!!!"
When you think about it long enough, there's lots of space for mind improvement
in your life! A great weight loser! A`plug for MENSA!

CHAPTER 11: "On Stage, Everyone!" . . . TutorTricks and Puzzles
We need more North American Geniuses! Canada and the U.S. are in deep trouble.
Get it together, be fast, quick, and highly professional. You'll never go hungry!
The Patter of Little Feet! Magical Calendar Feats! Ever heard of Prof. Trachtenberg?

CHAPTER 12: MR. POWER Himself . . . 142,857 !
Like a pretzel, he'll twist and turn so fast, he's one strange number!
Division? Just put him in Reverse!

CHAPTER 13: Magic Numbers in the Land of Math!*
Fast Squaring! Fractions! TUTOR Short Cut Fraction! Card Tricks!
Leonardo Fibonacc's Tricks! Intro view to Calculus!

CHAPTER 14: Trick or Treat! . . . SUPER MATH-E-MAGICIAN!!
Just a little Sleight of Mind! Strange numbers give strange answers! Think of a Card!
A short view of some Trigonometrical formulae! Intro to INTEGRAL CALCULUS!

CHAPTER 15: An Amazing MATH-E-MAGICS Memory Trick
Astound your spectators with an amazing mental acuity!

CHAPTER 16: SQUARES and SQUARE ROOTS
Now here's the pièce de resistance! Squares & Roots! Logarithms!
Read all about Einstein and his Uncle Itzak! Stage Caculator Supreme"!

CHAPTER 17: Meet the STAGE CALCULATORS – the MATH GREATS!!!
"Marvelous Griffith", Wallace Lee, (Calendar Trick!), Martin Gardner!

CHAPTER 18: CUBES and CUBE ROOTS
Rattle of cube roots like it's your close friend! And what about fifth roots?
Piece of cake! Nineteenth powers, anyone?

CHAPTER 19: Date Squares Anyone?
Date Squares, Logarithms, and Calculators? For real?

CHAPTER 20: Quite Quick TUTOR Short Cuts
Some Tricky Short Cuts! Cubes the Easy Way! Another Calendar Trick?

CHAPTER 21: A TUTOR of Short Cuts to Good Number Sense
Change a difficult number into an easy one! Combine Mental and written Math!

CHAPTER 22: TUTOR MATH of a Hundred Cuts!
Remember all these and you *are* a genius! But remember, there is always help!

CHAPTER 23: Multiplying in a Hurry!
Jakow Trachtenberg Rides Again! The Genius of the 40s is reawakened!

SOLUTIONS 24: Answers to Exercises & Index
How can we comment unless you get everything right!

GLOSSARY: G1 - G12
All you wanted to remember about Math things and were afraid to put to memory!

(NOTE: We're using the DECIMAL PAGE SYSTEM, e.g.: CHAPTER **6**.14-15)

PROLOGUE *

This acclaimed book, "SUPER MATH-E-MAGICS" *Without The Calculator,* is a very small part of the volumes of mathematical short-cuts and brain-teasing materials packed away by the author for future editions. He also plans to publish a series of intense, and thought-provoking High-Speed Calculating books. This is his first sortie in this form of math printing, and it will be received with enthusiasm by students and old professionals alike.

Now that you will be reading it, we ask you to re-read this wildly interesting and gripping subject matter, and slowly but surely, master all the new, deductive techniques. You will be coming into the society of learned savants and mathematicians of the Past. You already have rubbed shoulders with the Greats of Math and have been introduced to such notable persons as Galileo, G. A. Alberti, Carl Friedrich Gauss, Gelosia, Gerbert, Hylles, Pacioli, J. von Neumann, Zerah Colburn, Leonhard Euler, John Wallis and the 20th century genius, the late Jakow Trachtenberg, originator of a startling new system of arithmetic. We will demonstrate several of his findings in this book.

Naturally, as you progress into the inner sanctums of the mind-benders in future issues, we will cast aside the curtains of magical numbers and thought-provoking puzzles. You'll meet the "Great Pensa" mentor, who will beguile you with amazing stage performances. You will be given the tools of the mind to control your audiences in your class, neighbourhood, and be a shining example of what a little study can do for the mind. A real professional when it comes to juggling vast numbers in the mind. There are countless savants, others worth mentioning (and we fully intend to do that): the professional stage calculators, mental acrobats, et al.

The AMAZING MATH TUTOR is devised to "shock-it-to-you", to keep you waiting for the next issue which will come out on a bi-annual basis. There will be a minimum of two to three publications. It is the author's intention to revive the thinking apparatus we let fall into disrepair. We call it the "Brain", and we wish to re-instill the properties of number-sense to its own right, with its own values in commerce, creativity, thus restoring the pride which all the world holds for scientists, statisticians, chartered accountants, scholars which in all their wisdom have come to feel as they should. "I've got an intellect and I should be paid for its worth. I'm worth it!", as the saying goes.

The author looks forward to conducting the reader through an amazing list of mental giants and their gifts to us. They laboured hard into many a cold, starved nights to fulfill a dream of improving humanity. It's the least we can do to read of their exploits and benefit as a result of their untiring dedication to the one science that makes the world turn on its axis: MATHEMATICS!

SUPER MATH-E-MAGICS is also a vehicle upon which it will be worth while taking a ride. So take a chair, relax, grab a pencil, paper and read on.

-- Val Allan

***In case you're only reading this page, you're missing a good thing!**

About the Author . . .

STEPHEN LENAGHAN, a graduate of mathematics and languages of Jacques Cartier University of Montreal, joined the RCAF in March, 1940, and received his Observer (Navigator) Wing at Malton Airport, Weston, Ont., in August, 1940. In 1941, Steve resigned from the air force to become Chief Civilian Navigation Officer, RAF Ferry Command, Dorval, Que. After a stint of instruction, he re-enlisted in the RCAF, took a refresher and was posted overseas, RAF-attached Coastal Command in Great Britain. For a brief time was on loan as Navigation Instructor to USAF B-17 squadron in Northern Ireland. For a few months in 1944, he ferried bombers to the Middle East. At the end of the European war took discharge in January 1945.

Steve brings a wealth of knowledge in his writings, and has written a brace of fictional short stories. Now in his mid-70's, Steve Lenaghan, a Scarborough, Ontario resident, plans to follow up his SUPER MATH-E-MAGICS!!, the AMAZING MATH TUTOR with a PLUS Edition as soon as possible. "I've got enough research piled up for at least two or even more SUPER-PLUSES!"

INTRODUCTION

SUPER MATH-E-MAGICS *(by "The Old Math-Wizard!")* is really important in our day-to-day life! After all we don't want to be reliant on calculators and computers to do math for us. Right? **Correct!!** See, so far you're 100% on your test! Let's get your Tutor working!

Having that infernal calculator, small enough to carry in your pants' pocket or purse, may be a good reason to do sums without effort – but can you, if need be, be confident to think clearly in what we call "Number Sense" solutions to heady math questions?

Can we, as students in grade school, high school, college, or in a business environment do math in our head on a day-to-day basis? We have become totally dependent and lazy in our daily routines as new devices make us more reliant on the robot inventions developed by scientists and less reliant on our own mind.

By using the strategies in this course you will begin to have an overwhelming feeling of confidence and a sense of relief that "math isn't all *that* difficult!" Suddenly you'll realize how easy and how much fun math can really be.

If you are currently a student, whether it be elementary, middle school, high school or college, you will have no difficulty in applying the strategies taught in this course to your life each and everyday. After several hours of practice with these methods you will have learned a much easier way of looking at math and it will no doubt change that negative attitude you may have had about that lousy math. Did I hear you say, "I'll never understand math, I'm just a bum when it comes to algebra, or anything in the sciences."

Well, look no further, my friend. The time is now, get with it!

If you are a parent, and your son/daughter bring their problems to you, **take a decco at this course.** Get it for yourself if you lack the gift. Read this book before you let them in on it. Startle the children with sudden flashes of deep knowledge of problem-solving. Amaze the little folk with high-speed rapid calculating tricks. If you are not a parent, read through these next pages on your own. It will prove a strong point, that even the toughest of math problems can be made easy if it is approached differently

PREFACE

We all seem to be number conscious. We line up in the grocery by numbers according to their rules. "Check-out counter 1 and 2 for seniors with broken dozen purchases."

Shows with no names: just "No. 1 now showing 'Last Gun' ", etc. "Visa card number, please, social security identity." "No, madam, we can't let you in for your operation. You don't have your hospital number up-to-date. Sorry!"

We're just a pack of numbers to the many governments of the world. What ever happened to Mr. John Smith or Miss Edna Brassenberger. "Oh, you mean 567-456-1101, I saw him last week with his old girl friend, you know, the cute gal with a beautiful well-rounded figure, old 38-24-36 we all used to call her!"

We deal with numbers every day of our lives, yet we don't know their value other than the ever-popular buck. "I'll work for $14.00 an hour, or I'm walking." But if the boss says "I'll give you a 39% bonus over your $11.75 you're getting now" – you say "No way, Jose, $14. or I'm out of here." He smiles at you and says, "O.K., son, you drive a hard bargain." You should have taken the 39% raise. You got a lower raise just because you didn't know how to compute percentages of a number. Tough luck, fellow.

Schools are grinding out so-called scholars every day, every week, every year. Illiteracy and basic education are faulted by the system. Get those kids moving through the doors, and keep them moving till we can't see them. The government pays by the head, but doesn't guarantee the heads moved have any sense in them. **Number sense, that is!**

Some people can handle their day-to-day numerical problems adequately. They also handle adequately many troubling problems which they don't recognize as having numerical content. "What time is it?" They can tell you if the change is right. If something costs $4.95 they know it's going to come out over the $5.00 plus or something – but just how much is that a "something?" Well, they leave that to the cash register and never bat an eyelash to enquire what percent is that GST or provincial sales tax and what does it come to. OK, so it's printed on the sales receipt. The clerk could have made an error, but you never bother to glance to see if there was the possibility of a human error. *Garbage in* means *garbage out.* The old computer slogan.

If there really was such a drastic error, we all would complacently accept that error of the business with whom we are dealing.

Number problems fall into two classifications: a "high" and a "low." Big deal, you say. Perhaps that's true, *it is a big deal*!

Consider the *Low* Problem: This definitely concerns the educationalist. Pupils in normal-to-bright levels get by even if their teachers are not an inspiration to them. The parents, the family, the D-report cards, those "notes" Johnny or Sally could do much better . . . keep the ship of learning on an even keel.

There is a serious problem with the "low", sometimes less able children – *they are not stupid*. These are children just unsuited for the type of instruction presented by their tutors and teachers. We have conventional methods for presenting facts and theory in the school levels. Some just cannot conform to the teaching applications as now presented with the hodge-podge curriculum of school boards extant in North America.

Without experimentation into the difficulties of students who have disabilities of comprehension, the numerous failures being pushed out into the workplace will continue to exacerbate. The widespread conflict in the minds of mathematically-impoverished minds of these children will escalate into a division of the middle-class societies. So let's face the facts. Math, as it is known, must be deliberately researched and modified to allow growing children a chance to have "**Number Sense**" as its basis. Before we go stuffing some of that geometry, algebra, trigonometry, calculus, etc., let's teach them the fundamentals properly. School boards must be prepared to experiment, provide necessary funding to remedy the ills that students suffer in the growth of their brain power.

The problem **"High"** or " in the middle" is much more general and yet not as easy to define. "It can be said to be that, despite all the efforts made by teachers of one generation after another, an organized understanding of the various aspects of numbers is almost universally lacking.) It exists only amongst those who have a special interest in mathematical studies. Indeed, there seems to be a positive resistance to almost all the efforts made to persuade people at large that an attempt to learn more about numbers in any organized way is worth the effort. We accept the necessity for being able to tell the time, read a railway timetable, handle cash efficiently, and the like, but these activities are seen from a purely practical standpoint – they are not thought to be of any conceptual interest, and they are entirely divorced from each other.

Mathematics as an educational pastime is unpopular!

Say "Math" and the kids say "Yukk!" Conversation comes to a dead halt. Turning away to find other pastimes they fade into the wallpaper. Its mention is guaranteed to put a stop to any frolicking in the house. The only time they will countenance that word is in school. It is not merely that it is a dull subject, but also that it is thought to be largely unnecessary in regular life, except maybe for extra gas allowance on the weekend, or the odd case of beer or an ice cream soda for the girl or boy friend on a date.

As we open these course pages, please refrain from any comments of "boring", "who cares", what's new about that". You will be surprised that you knew so little about Mathematics. The research of many years and through the accomplishments of so many mathematicians, both present and in our dim past, has caused the author to collect an amazing selection of mind-boggling high-speed mathematical tricks, acts and school-room problem-solving strategies worthy of your interest and admiration. This course is more than a treatise on mathematical revelations. It entreats the students of mathematics to seek further for themselves to reach the pinnacle of perfection.

Once you have put to memory and successfully completed the brain-teasing math games, the short-cut methods that will increase your memory to new levels, then you will feel that sense of accomplishment that is your due. You will have become a true mathematician. Works from Abel, Absolon, Alcuin of York to Wessel, Xerxes and Zeno of Elea will unfold and make your mind glow with admiration for the past masters of numerical invention that makes the present world the wonderful place that it is. Genius reigns in the Math World. Why can't you aspire to also belong in it?

To go further into this Preface would take up too much space, and leave nothing for study space. So, finally, with a deep breath, a clear mind, let's find out how much we really know. Firstly, about the basic math level of the old mind, and for the beginner, an explanation of the foot holds we will find on this mountain of figuring. We will attempt to expand your knowledge, hone your wit, and expand your Number Sense, and make you a Front Runner, who shall strive eagerly, earnestly to become the ***"Perfect, Compleat Whiz Kid on the Block!"*** Yeah!

The future belongs to the mathematically skilled.

Mathematics: The Invisible Filter, p. 26
Toronto Board of Education

There are few occupations that do not use mathematics in some form. Future career opportunities are severely limited by students who avoid mathematics. In order to keep their options open, students should be encouraged to take as many mathematics and mathematics-related courses as possible.

Intervention strategies to prevent future dropouts should be provided in the elementary years. Grades 6 to 8 are seen as target years for interventions to ensure that all students are made aware of the usefulness of mathematics in everyday life and in careers.

Try this for an attention-grabbing opener.

Turn to the Squaring section of this workbook and read through it once, (that's all it takes). Gather your children about you and ask them the following question: Turn to Page 2.6.

What's the square of 66?
What's the square of 93?
(or what's 17 x 14?) See page 5.1.

You'll know what they're going to say . . . **"Are you kidding, what do you think I am? A blinking ruddy genius! I *don't know* what the answer is."**

Here's you chance, Mom and Dad. Go for the big time. You're in command now. The children will look at you in a different light from now on.

(P.S.): All you younger generations, kids and young folk, please take it easy on your parents. It just could be that you got to this course before they were aware of it.

Thought for Today:

There are people who try to match their ways to the world about them. Those are the followers. Then there are those who strike out boldly against the tide of world ideas. Those are the great workers of change and progress. Which are you?

Anon.

So let's get the course on the road!!!

I THOUGHT I'D GET THIS GUYS ATTENTION BEFORE I HIT HIM WITH THE MATH

Chapter 1

INTERESTED IN A QUICK LOOK?

Let's agree right here and now – This book takes an odd-ball attitude when it comes to Math! If we are agreed on that, then let's get right at it! Thanks for listening!

It's usually difficult to put your head back into the school books when you've been away too long. Undoubtedly you will say that's kid stuff. Is it really? Let's see you square 36 without a calculator. What's the square root of 256? 289^2? Need we go on? Just relax and enjoy this book. Wander through it at first and when something seem interesting and catches your imagination, let your youth flood from your pent-up memories. G'wan, it's play-time for your own benefit! Let's review, huh? **AMAZING MATH TUTOR's Short Cut Methods of Hi-Speed Multiplication.** A "short method" shortens an operation considerably, or at least it should make the operation much easier to perform. Some short methods are worthwhile and easy to remember as we will show here.

1) To multiply by 10, or any multiple of 10 by itself, such as 10, 100, 1,000: add as many zeros to the multiplicand as there are zeros in the multiplier.

Example. Multiply 528 by (a) 10; (b) 100; (c) 1,000;

Solution: (a) 5,280; (b) 52,800; (c) 528,000.

2) To multiply by any number whose value is within 5 units of any multiple of 10 by itself, multiply by the **nearest** multiplier of 10 (as in the preceding example); then multiply by the unit figure and add (or subtract) this result.

Example. Multiply: (a) 792 by 101; (b) 84 by 99; (c) 432 by 102

Solution:

(a) 79,200
+ 792
79,992

EXPLANATION: 792 x 100 = 79,200
79,200 + 792 = 79,992.

(b) 8,400
– 84
8,316

EXPLANATION: 84 x 100 = 8,400.
8,400 – 84 = 8,316.

(c) 43,200
+ 864
44,064

EXPLANATION: 432 x 100 = 43,200
432 x 2 = 864.
43,200 + 864 = 44,064.

3) To multiply by any two digit number whose tens digit is 1: multiply by the units digit; write this partial product one place to the right of the multiplicand; and add.

Example. Multiply 353 by 17.

Solution. 353 x 7 = 2471. Write this partial product one place to the right of the multiplicand as shown at the left, and add. This method saves the time it takes to write the multiplicand and the multiplier.

3 53
2,471
6,001

4) To multiply by number of two digits whose unit digit is 1: multiply by the tens digit; write this partial product one place to the left of the multiplicand; and add.

Example. Multiply 765 by 71.

Solution. 765 x 7 = 5,355. Write this partial product one place to the left of the multiplicand, as shown at the left, and add. Again you note that this method simply saves the time it takes to write the multiplicand and the multiplier.

765
53 55
54,315

5) To multiply a two-digit number by 11:

a) If the sum of the two digits in the multiplicand is less than 10, add the two digits. Then place this sum between the two digits of the multiplicand.

Example. Multiply 54 by 11.

Solution. Add 5 + 4 = 9. Hence the answer is 594.

b) If the sum of the two digits in the multiplicand is 10 or more, add the two digits. Then place the units digit of this sum between the two digits of the multiplicand and increase the tens digit of the multiplicand by one.

Or, add the right-hand neighbor (N). Think of 54 as 0540 x 11. The zeros are only unique to your imagination.

Eg, 4 + 0(N) = **4,** write **4.** 5 + 4(N) = **9.** Write **9** left of **4.** 0 + 5(N) = **5.**
Ans. 594.

Again, **Example:** 0 6784 0 x 11 = **4** + 0 = **4** write **4**
8 + 4 = **12,** carry the 1, write **2**
7 + 8 = **15** plus 1 = **16,** carry the 1, write **6**
6 + 7 = 13 plus 1 = **14,** carry the 1, write **4**
0 + 6 = 6 plus 1 = **7,** write **7**

Answer: 74624. (when we have a remainder, we write **'r'**.)

Exercise: Multiply: (a) 69 by 1 l; (b) 2458 x 11:

Solution:

(a) 6 + 9 = 15. Place 5 between 9 and 6. 6 + **r1** = 7. Answer is 759.
Or (9 + 0 = **9**; 6 + 9 = **15**; 0 + 6 + **r1** = 7. Ans: 759.

(b) 2458 = Think floating 0's at each end of numbers. Add rt-hand neighbor. Write as you add, 8 + 0 = **8**; 5 + 8 = 13, write **3,** carry 1, 4 + 5 = 9 + r1 = 10, write **0**, carry 1, 2 + 4 = 6 + r1 = **7**, 0 + 2 = **2.**

Answer: 27038.

6. While we are on the subject of adding the right hand neighbor, **let us consider 11's neighbor -> 12.**

The rule now is **double** the number and add the (N) neighbor.

Let's multiply 468 x 12 = ?

Consider 468 as 0 468 0 x 12. So let's kick off with the right-hand 8. Twice 8 is **16 + zero (rt-hand neighbor/N) = 16**, write down **6**, carry 1. Moving slowly left, double 6 = **12 + 8(N) + 1** (rem.) = **21;** write down **1**, carry 2. Left again, double the 4 = **8 + 6(N) + 2** (r) = **16**, write down 6, carry 1; last motion, double 0 = **0 + 4(N)** + 1 (r) = 5616.

Answer is **5616.**

7) To multiply by 5, 25, 50, 250:

(a) To multiply by 5, add a zero to the multiplicand and divide by 2.

b) To multiply by 25, add two zeros to multiplicand and divide by 4.

c) To multiply by 50, add two zeros to multiplicand and divide by 2.

d) To multiply by 250, add three zeros to multiplicand, divide by 4.

Example. Multiply: (a) 129 by 5; (b) 128 by 25; (c) 150 by 50:
(d) 192 by 250.

Solution. (a) 1,290 ÷ 2 = 645; (b) 12,800 ÷ 4 = 3,200;
(c) 15,000 ÷ 2 = 7,500; (d) 192,000 ÷ 4 = 48,000

EXERCISE 1

Using short cuts perform the indicated operation.

1. 63 x 10	8. 555 x 12	15. 519 x 61	22. 363 x 103
2. 73 x 100	9. 796 x 12	16. 875 x 51	23. 536 x 99
3. 589 x 1,000	10. 649 x 15	17. 443 x 41	24. 491 x 98
4. 618 x 11	11. 779 x 18	18. 455 x 71	25. 582 x 55
5. 367 x11	12. 266 x 19	19. 978 x 91	26. 549 x 25
6. 295 x 11	13. 392 x17	20. 454 x 101	27. 285 x 50
7. 668 x 11	14. 467 x 31	21. 279 x 102	28. 348 x 25

8.0 **Complementary Method of Multiplication:** In order to promote the use of the Hindu-Arabic numerals, the medieval teacher did not require his students to learn the multiplication table beyond 5 x 10. To multiply under this limitation, various methods were developed. Of these, the best known is the Complementary method. It has endured to modern times because it lends itself to finger reckoning. **To multiply any two digits, find the complements of these digits.** (See Chapter 5.6)

Multiplying the complements. The units digit of this product is the units digit of the answer. Mentally, carry the tens digit of this product and add it to the difference between either one of the two given digits and the complement of the other. The result is the tens digit in the answer.

Example: Multiply: (a) 7 x 6; (b) 8 x 7.

Solution. (a) The complement of 7 is 3 and the complement of 6 is 4.

7	3	The product 3 x 4 = 12. Write 2, carry 1. Add 1 to the
6	4	difference between 7 – 4 or 6 – 3. The sum, 4 (3 + 1), is the
4	2	tens digit.

(b) The complement of 8 is 2 and the complement of 7 is 3.

8	2	The product 2 x 3 = 6. Write 6, nothing to carry. The
7	3	difference between 8 – 3 or 7 – 2 is 5, the tens digit of the
5	6	answer.

As stated above, this method lends itself to finger reckoning. To obtain 9 x 7 find their respective complements, 1 and 3. Raise one finger on one hand and 3 fingers on the other hand to denote these complements. The sum of the closed fingers, 4 + 2 = 6, gives the tens digit. The product of the raised fingers, 1 x 3 = 3, give the units digit. Therefore, the answer is 63.

If the multiplicand and the multiplier have the same number of digits and if their complements are small, this method can be extended to find the product of larger numbers. The product of the complements gives the units digit, or the units and tens digit, in the answer. The difference between any one of the given numbers and the complement of the other gives the digits at the left in the answer. The product must have twice as many digits as the multiplicand. We fill in the necessary number of zeros between the complementary product and the difference.

Example: Multiply: (a) 98 by 96; (b) 997 by 986.

Solution. (a) The complement of 98 is 2, the complement of 96 is 4. The product of these complements is 4 x 2 - 8. The difference 98 – 4 = 96 – 2 = 94. the answer must have four digits, place one zero between 94 and 8, obtains the answer **9,408.**

98 2
96 4
94 0 8

(b) The complement of 997 is 3 and the complement of 986 is 14. The product of these complements is 14 x 3 = 42. The difference 997 – 14 or 986 – 3 = 983. the answer need six digits, place one zero between 983 and 42, obtaining the answer **983,042.**

997 3
986 14
983 042

Early Methods of Multiplication. After much trial and error, mankind finally created our present system of multiplication. Some of those early methods are illustrated here and can give an enriched understanding of the principles used currently.

Gelosia Method. The first printed case was found in *The Treviso Arithmetic,* printed c.1480. The Italian word *gelosia* means a lattice work of a window. It received this name because the calculations are noted in a framework resembling a window glass grating.

Figure 1 shows the multiplication of 676 by 49 as it would have been demonstrated in the Treviso arithmetic. For purposes of comparison, the operation performed in our modern system is shown at the left of the figure. The framework consists of a rectangle divided into cells by horizontal and vertical lines. The number of columns, 3, is the same as the number of digits in the multiplicand, 676. The number of rows, 2, is equal to the number of digits in the multiplier, 49. The multiplicand is written across the top, each digit heading a column.

If the multiplier is written down the right side, as shown in Fig. 1, diagonals are drawn upward from left to right, dividing each cell into two parts. Each single-digit combination is written in a cell; the units digit in the lower portion and the tens, if any, in the upper portion.

Example: Using the ***Gelosia method,*** multiply 676 by 49.

Solution. Beginning at the upper right-hand-corner cell, 4 x 6 = 24; write 2 in the upper portion and 4 in the lower portion. 4 x 7 = 28; write 2 in the upper chamber, 8 in the lower, and continue on in all cells. Start adding diagonally from lower right-hand corner. The answer appear around the outside perimeter, left and bottom.

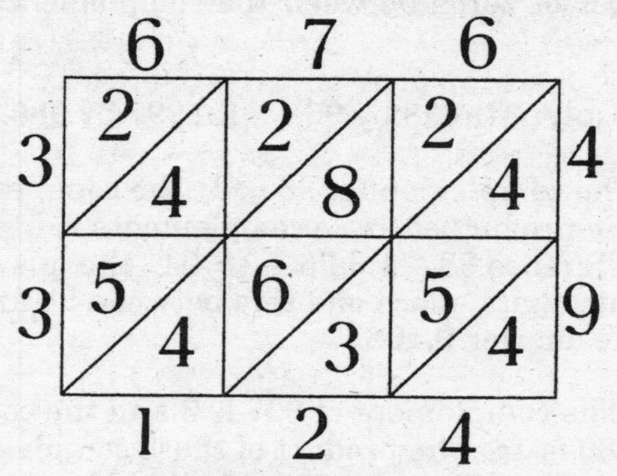

EXERCISE 2-a

Perform the indicated operation using the Gelosio method.

1. 423 x 29
2. 547 x 47
3. 461 x 26
4. 2738 x 46
5. 3614 x 44
6. 459 x 281
7. 2845 x 323
8. 5237 x 40
9. 175 x 9
10. 49 x 27
11. 66 x 46
12. 675 x 72
13. 657 x 26
14. 458 x 65
15. 144 x 37
16. 427 x 38
17. 289 x 25
18. 477 x 34
19. 543 x 46
20. 677 x 123
21. 246 x 234
22. 357 x 345
23. 2575 x 213
24. 4695 x 258

2-b. Perform the indicated operation, using Complementary method:

1. 7 x 9
2. 6 x 7
3. 96 x 98
4. 96 x 87
5. 96 x 97
6. 998 x 995
7. 999 x 993
8. 996 x 987

3. Checking Multiplication. *Casting out Nines.* Since multiplication is communicative, that is, the product is the same regardless of the order in which the numbers are multiplied. The operation can be checked by interchanging the multiplicand and the multiplier. Thus, the product 146 x 128 can be checked as shown below. Multiply in two ways, as follows:

```
  146        128
  128        146
 1168        768
 292        512
146        128
18688      18688
```

The methods of casting out nines (9) and also casting out elevens (11) are much quicker and easier this way. Several methods can be used to check multiplication because the product of the check numbers of the multiplicand and the multiplier is equal to the check number of the product .

Example. Multiply 146 x 128 and check by : (a) casting out 9's, (b) casting out 11's.

Solution. (a) Check number of 146 is 1 + 4 + 6 = 11 or 1 + 1 = 2, and the check number of 128 is 1 + 2 + 8 = 11 or 1 + 1 = 2. The product of the check numbers is 2 x 2 = 4. The check number of 18,688 = 1 + 8 + 6 + 8 + 8 = 31 = 3 + 1 = 4. Since the product of the check numbers of the multiplicand and the multiplier is equal to the check number of product, therefore the answer is right, correct, true.

```
  146
  128
 ----
 1168
 292
146
-----
18688
```

EXERCISE 3

Multiply and check by (a) casting out nines; (b) casting out elevens.

1. 85 x 23	5. 108 x 78	9. 954 x 423	13. 4494 x 275
2. 739 x 43	6. 789 x 937	10. 4346 x 375	14. 4193 x 878
3. 686 x 36	7. 393 x 128	11. 4193 x 403	15. 6450 x 238
4. 591 x 31	8. 396 x 106	12. 6450 x 719	16. 9876 x 1234

17. If one Bic pen costs 18 cents, how much would 19 dozen pencils cost?

18. If each basket contains 14 dozen peppers, what is the cost to the grocer if he has to pay 17 cents each?

19. How many minutes are there in the month of July?

20. If a page contains 63 lines, how many lines are in a book of 165 pages?

21. The wheel of an bus traveling at 65 miles per hour makes 869 revolutions per minute. How many revolutions will it make in 3 hour?

22. If a rocket on its way to Mars, carrying an monkey, travels at the rate of 1,346 miles per minute, how far will it travel in 2 hours and 37 minutes?

23. A store clerk dividing a number by 3.5, should have multiplied, obtaining 23. What should have been correct answer?

24. Two cattlemen, 32 miles apart, are traveling toward each other, each traveling at the rate of 4 miles per hour. A pigeon, carrying messages between both riders, flying at the rate of 12 miles an hour, flies back and forth between the two men until they meet. How far does the tired old bird fly? (By the way, they ate the pigeon for supper.)

50-MINUTE MATH WIZARD!

All you have to do to make big money is rent a hall, plan a video, and become a Math Whizzard. Recently, in these past two years, the North American continent TV viewers were regaled with several whiz math types. For a paltry $80 (US) or so, they taught children, on different networks, how to cross-multiply two digit numbers; multiply some numbers within a close range value of 6 to 8 away from 100. Both even had audiences of over 30 or more noisy receptive kids.

This crowd lent some validity to what cost the unsuspecting public a real outlay for a series of four "stage calculating" tricks included in this book (at no extra charge, I might add). We leave you to judge if it was really practical (academically) in giving any worthwhile school value for the money requested. I admit the presenters of these shows that appeared throughout the countries mentioned had some smarts. But they only excelled within the framework of stage calculators. With a gimmick like that, if you can rattle off 2, 4, 6, 8, to a 100, that is not intelligence at work, but years of repetitive practice in a narrow corridor of rote. Certainly, it was entertainment some sort, perhaps, but assuredly not suitable to be an enhancement to one's brain power. Let's review one act they used. It's tongue in cheek, and only covers the fractions in mathematics.

How many ways can you divide a Camel?

Curtain Rises: ("Amazing" appears!

The show opens with the savant calling for 17 kids from the audience, (not just any audience, but a hand-picked audience).

The stage calculator tells how an old man by the name of Benbula, who is dying, wants to leave his sons a fortune in camels (in our country it would have been acres of oats). He tells a wise man of his problem and says in a gasping tone, "I have three boys but I have only 17 camels. I want you to give my first, Sammy, one-half (he's the oldest, he's the camp doctor, you know!); Bern, he's to get a third (Bern is a good boy, but he plays too much rock band stuff), and Hassine (well, we won't talk about him, he dropped out of everything, except an elevator, which his good mama often wished), so give him one-ninth!"

"A ninth?", the wise man asks, "a ninth of a camel! Sheesh! If that Camel was a cigarette, that would only make a couple of puffs."

But anyway the wise man thinks about it for a week, while the old man gets weaker. That following weekend, the wise man shows up leading a bent-up camel with half a hump. "Benny," says the aging learned savant. "Have I got a deal for you!"

"Remember what I said last week. You can't divide 17 camels by a half, a third and one-ninth. Remember? You don't remember? Anyway you did. Well, I'm going to throw in this healthy looking. fresh young camel and make it 18 camels.

"Now we can divide your 17 camels plus mine up fairly. We make 17 + 1 = 18 camels. Right? OK, one half to Sammy. he gets 9 camels. one-third of 18 equals 6, they go to Bern. OK? one ninth of 18 gets 2, right? Hassine gets that. Are you listening? Hey, Ben, this is no time to fall asleep on me, wake up!

"So we add the camels up, and guess what? I got one camel left over, mine! So you're satisfied and I'm a wise man. So, old friend, I'll just take back my healthy-looking, young fresh camel and be off." With that he goes into the herd of camels and picks out a young, healthy looking camel and has one of the old man's good-looking young wives help him take the frisky camel home.

As the wise man leaves the compound, a small girl races after him and his camel. "Wait! Wait!" The wise man stops as the breathless girl slides to a halt. "So, what's it is?" The girl gasps and, taking a deep gulp of air, says, "Master Benbula's second wife just gave birth to twin sons!"

The wise man mounts the camel, slips his arm around the young wife's waist and gallops off into the sunset, and is never seen again. (or something.) Well, maybe that wasn't the way the lady told it on the TV, but that was how the problem was demonstrated.

The second mental trick was adding a column of three figures, three numbers wide.

$$\begin{array}{r} 325 \\ 236 \\ \underline{174} \end{array}$$

The addition started from the top left side of the first column, and was addressed as follows:

"300 plus 200 is 500 plus 100 is 600", (then going to the top of the tens' column, continued: "600 and 20 plus 30 is 650 plus 70 is 720," and then moving to the units' column: "720 and 5 is 725, and 6 makes it 731, plus 4 equals 735." (*much applause*) Like wow!

Well, that's novel, but that technique has been known for about five hundred years, or even longer. It's in the book!

We then were conducted in the very fine art of multiplying two double numbers. The numbers were;

```
  3 4
x 2 6
-----
```

4 x 6 = 24, write 4 and carry 2 as remainder. Cross multiply 3 x 6 = 18, 2 x 4 = 8 + 18 + 2 (remainder) = 28, write 8 and carry 2, and lastly, 2 x 3 = 6 plus 2 (rem.) = 8. Therefore, answer is 884. *(applause)*

Negative addition was mentioned rather than subtracting. That method is commonly known in business transaction in many parts of the world. Instead of subtracting, the question is asked mentally: "How much do we add to the lower number to reach the top number in value? E.g., rather than 8 take away 5 equals 3 – if that's the way you think now – I would have to add 3 to 5 to get the 8 above it. That's all." *(applause)*

On the fourth method talked about. the multiplication always centered about 100, plus or minus. No mention was made of any numbers above or below the value of 10 or 12. Now you can't go through life in that lane only.

Let me talk about their complementary/supplementary (under 100/over 100) multiplication method.

If you multiply 96 and 94, for instance, you line up the figures so:

```
(100 –  96 = 4)   96   4
(100 –  94 = 6)   94   6
```

"Well, If you take either criss-cross answer of 96 – 6, or 94 – 4, both will equal 90. That's the first left hand part of your answer. To get the other right half, multiply 4 x 6 = 24. That's all there is, there ain't no more. Answer is 9024." *(more applause)*

That was the complementary method. Now it's the same for supplementary multiplying. Instead of subtracting, you add.

Multiply 109 and 102. Line up the figures like this:

```
(109 – 100 = 9)   109   9
(102 – 100 = 2)   102   2
```

"Now what do we do?" Heck, I know, this time I was watching! If you take either criss-cross answer of 109 + 2, or 102 + 9, both equal 111, the left hand side of the answer. You still multiply vertically the 9 and the 2, giving you 18 as the right hand answer. Then, the answer is 11,118. Correct? Easy, isn't it?

Again, this knowledge has been in the books for countless years, generations, and along come these readily available tricks on TV that generated sales of this vaguely useful knowledge and fortunes are reaped. Or were we raped financially!?

Squares and cubes are done with ease. Memorize the squares of 1, 2, 3. 4. 5, 6, 7, 8, 9, and the cubes and fifth powers of these same numbers (it takes but a half hour and you're an expert).

Why aren't these little tricks shown for babies to play with at age 3, or 4, or even 5. We can all become whiz kids if given the props or toys that would lead to memory tricks. Rote is looked upon as trash nowadays. If you cannot visualize the number set, then you have no number sense. Bosh! Untrue! Genius is the ever-expanding of the walls of the brain. Not in size, but in the memory banks of the individual. If given the chance we could all have read the classics by at least 4 years of age, and helped solve the mysteries of the universe. We have, figuratively, a sponge in our head which will soak up all you can put in it, and by the rote method no less. If you are given the right teacher, or an attentive instructor, the sky's the limit!

Oh, yes! One other trick shown for $80 (US) was how to square any number ending in 5. Not 6 or 9, just 5. If you are squaring 65, 55, 35, the trick is to add l to the left hand number, therefore 65 squared becomes 6 x (6 + l) 7 = 42 stuck to the left of the constant 25. Then the answer for 65^2 is 4225. 55^2 is 3025, and 35^2 is 1225; square 85?

$$8+1=9\times 8=72(25)$$

30-odd pages of motivational bunk for this marvelous education were strictly channeled at the kids: "Keep reading, working, and looking for the next $80(US) lessons that may be coming soon!"

This isn't the way to interested minds of young children. They need mind food and lots of it. They're eager to learn, and not just a couple of tricks. They want the works. They're entitled to be treated as students, not country-bumpkins at a bazaar in the back woods. Let's give them their rein. Let them rove in the libraries. They are at school to succeed. As teachers, let's bring back rote, and get rid of those infernal calculators. **Learn the basics first, then whatever!**

ALRIGHT CLASS... IT'S BACK TO BASICS
2+2=4

Chapter 2

What's the Basis of Arithmetic?

"Reeling and Writhing, of course, to begin with," the Mock-Turtle replied, "and the different branches of Arithmetic – Ambition, Distraction, Uglification, and Derision."

LEWIS CARROLL – *Alice in Wonderland,* Chapter X.

When all of us were very young, we were taught the addition tables first. $1 + 1 = 2$, $1 + 2 = 3$, and so on. We were also instructed to reverse the numbers, and lo! and behold, $2 + 4 = 6$ and $4 + 2 = 6$. We were told in words of one syllable that this worked the same for all like additions. Two or more numbers arrived at the same answer when added from either direction. This was the first strategy pumped into our brain.

To put this statement into mathematicians' logic, it reads like this: ***the sum is independent of the order of the terms.*** This first law was called ***the commutative law,*** and can be written in these symbols,

$$a + b + c + d = d + c + b + a = x \quad \text{(x is the correct answer).}$$

In keeping with this statement, $(8 + 2) + 3 = 8 + (2 + 3) = 13$; it's of no consequence which order we add these numbers. Each way it comes out 13. Therefore addition is also called *associative.* If we go further into higher groups of addition we see:

$$\begin{array}{r} 32 \\ 18 \\ 27 \\ \hline 77 \end{array}$$

Take a deep look at the make-up of this operation:

$$32 + 18 + 27 =$$
$$(30 + 2) + (10 + 8) + (20 + 7) =$$
$$(30 + 10 + 20) + (2 + 8 + 7) =$$
$$(30 + 30) + (10 + 7) =$$
$$60 + 17 = 77$$

You can now see the *commutative and associative processes* in action. If multiplication and addition get together on the same question, another rule comes into force. We can find the product 6 x (4 + 5) in either of two ways. (6 x 9 = 54), or (24 + 30 = 54). So multiplication is ***distributive*** with respect to addition. Another way to express it in algebraic terms is:

$$a \times (b + c) = ab + ac$$

We've allowed *'a'* to distribute its value within the brackets.

So now we have *associative, commutative and distributive* properties of this operation upon which the basic principles of Arithmetic are based.

Fun Time (for a moment) . . . The Repetitious Number !

An unusual parlor trick is performed as follows. Ask spectator A to write down any three-digit number, and then to repeat the digits in the same order to make a six-digit number (e.g., 394,394). With your back turned so that you cannot see the number, ask A to pass the sheet of paper to spectator B, who is asked to divide the number by 7.

"Don't worry about any remainder," you caution him/her, "because there won't be any." B is surprised to discover that you are right (e.g., 394,394 divided by 7 is 56,342). Without telling you the result, he/she passes it on to spectator C, who is told to divide it by 11. Once again you state that there will be no remainder, and this also proves correct (56,342 divided by 11 is 5,122).

With your back still turned, and no knowledge whatever of the figures obtained by these computations, you direct a fourth spectator, D, to divide the last result by 13. Again the division comes out even (5,122 divided by 13 is 394). This final result is written on a slip of paper which is folded and handed to your assistant. Without opening it, let her pass it on to spectator A.

"Open this," you tell him, "and you will find your original three-digit number." Proof that the trick cannot fail to work regardless of the digits chosen by the first spectator.

Let's Review TUTOR SHORT CUTS in Division

Divisibility tests are quick tools to answer simple questions about a number's factors. Here are some handy tests to keep in mind:

How to tell if a number is divisible by:

2 – If it is an even number, i. e. ends in 2, 4, 6, 8, or 0.

3 – If the sum of the digits of the number is divisible by 3.

4 – If the last two digits of the number represents a number that is divisible by 4.

6 – If the number meets the tests for 2 and 3.

8 – If the last three digits of the number represents a number divisible by 8.

9 – If the sum of the digits of the number is divisible by 9.

5 – If the number ends in 0 or 5.

10 – If the number ends in 0.

*11– Find the sum of the digits in even place-value powers of ten.
Find the sum of the digits in odd place value powers of ten. If the difference of these two sum is divisible by 11, the number is then divisible by 11.

12 – If the numbers meet the above tests for 3 and 4.

*11 – 10^5, 10^4, 10^3, 10^2, 10^1, 10^0. The even and odd place-value powers refer to the exponents – 0, 1, 2, 3, 4, 5, 6, on & on.

Back to Work, Folks! Let's Try . . .

HOW TO SQUARE ANY NUMBER UNDER 100

Squaring Any Number Under 100 . . . the SHORT-CUT Method
(Using the *Math-Wizard's* UP SOME – DOWN SOME!)

Now we come to our more general short cut for mentally squaring any two-digit number. not just numbers ending in 5. ***The Up Some/Down Some Method*** itself is best understood by studying a simple example.

Example:
Square 18 mentally. Replace 18 x 18 by 18 + (2) = 20 . . . **Up Some** and (18 – (2) = 16 (**Down Some**, for a first estimate).

Therefore, (20) (16) = 320, that's close, but not close enough!

Square the difference number (2^2) for a correction to be added to the first estimate. $2^2 = 2 \times 2 = 4$. Add this correction of 4 to the first estimate.

320 + 4 = 324 (answer)

(alternate method would have been **The Boomerang Way**. See page 37-.)

What we have done is to replace the original 18^2 by a first estimate, which is a fast mental calculation, plus a small correction, which is known. In practice, both parts of the answer can be found mentally and handled in one continuous operation. In this example, there is normal calculation as such. The answer is found "by slipping the digit 4 (2^2) into the units place. These mental calculations always take much less time than the usual longhand squaring process. Remember that this method is exact, even though it might appear to be just an estimate. In most cases, the first estimate alone (320 above) is sufficiently accurate for the purpose in mind.

Let's try a more difficult number.

Example: Square 24. *Go up 4 units* to 28 and *down 4 units* to 20:

28 x 20 = 560– all mental steps; (4 x 4 = 16) + 560 = 576.

Let's try a still more difficult number.

Example: Square 36. *Go up 4 units* to 40 and *down 4 units* to 32. ***(Note: when you multiply two numbers, always place the number with a zero last. It's easier to think downwards. You only have one calculation to do!)***

Step 1 – (Mental multiplication) 32 x 40 = 1280.
Step 2 – 4 x 4 = 16 (mental operation)

Final think: 1280 + 10 + 6 = 1296 (mental operation)

As you notice the "Up – Down" method is useful for squares. **Step 1** – (raising the square up by a figure or two figures works with most squares.) The square correction of **Step 2** can be used either to refine the third place in each example in order to get the exact answer. It depends on whether you need a guesstimate or an exact result.

This method is perfectly general and quite exact. It can really be used to square any two numbers under 100. However, the mental effort is increased somewhat as the numbers get higher than 60. To show this, consider a square between 50 and 60.

Example:
Square 56. Go down 6 units to 50, up 6 units to 62.

62 x 50 = 3100 (add 2 zeros, divide by2);
6 x 6 = 36
56^2 = 3136 (answer)

Notice that it is much easier to multiply by 50 than by 60.

Now square a number over 60.

Example: Square 66 mentally. Go up 4 units to 70 and down 4 units to 62. (Do this strictly by mental process.)

$$\begin{aligned} 62 \times 70 &= 4340 \\ 4 \times 4 &= \underline{\quad 16} \\ 66^2 &= 4356 \end{aligned}$$

But the operation of multiplying 62 x 7 mentally is a little difficult for beginners. The best way is still mentally:

Two ways: 7 x 6 = 42, think 420, plus 7 x 2 = 14; 420 + 14 = 430 or really 4340 in round figures, now add 4^2, for the ups and down motions. Or this version: 7 x 60 = **420**; 7 x 2 = 14; 420 + 14 = **434** (*think a zero*) 434(0) + $\mathbf{4^2}$ = **4356.** (correct answer)

Sometimes it's easier to square higher numbers, especially near 100.

Example: Square 93. Go up 7 units to 100; down 7 units to 86.

$$\begin{aligned} 86 \times 100 &= 8600 \\ 7 \times 7 &= \underline{\quad 49} \\ 93^2 &= 8649 \end{aligned}$$

In this case, the correction 49 fits right into place at the end of the number. This time we did not use the nearest multiple of 10, which would have been 90. That is because (86 x 100) + 49 = 8649 is much easier to calculate than (96 x 90) + 9 = 8649.

Later we will consider complementary and supplementary multiplication. We always call this area of multiplication around, above and below 100, the Complementary and the Supplementary Methods. (See Chapter 5, p. 54)

For mental calculations, it is desirable to choose one multiplier to be of such numbers as 20, 50, or even 10 for much easier multiplication. You can go above 10 units to arrive there. Try this one.

Example: Square 87. Go up 13 points to reach 100 and then go down 13 points the other way and get 74.

$$74 \times 100 = 7400$$
$$13 \times 13 = \underline{\ 169}$$
$$87^2 = 7569$$

Example: Square 89. Go up 11 units to 100 and down 11 units to 78.

$78 \times 100 = 7800$ (perform mentally
$11 \times 11 = \underline{\ 121}$ (perform mentally)
$88^2 = 7921$ (change the 8 to 9, add 21)

Compare this calculation with the following alternate approach: Go up 1 unit to 90 and down 1 unit to 88.

$88 \times 90 = 7920$ (more difficult)
$1 \times 1 = \underline{\quad\quad 1}$ (easier
$89^2 = 7921$ (easier)

The same answer, 7921, is obtained but the first two steps vary. It's best to suit your own particular abilities. Either approach is better than trying to square 88 the conventional way – mentally. However, you could use the Short Cut 60, on page 22.6.

By now, you should be able to square such sizable numbers as 194 and 209 by inspection. Keep "Up and Down Some" in mind!

$$194^2 = (188)(200) + 6^2 = 37{,}600 + 36 = 37{,}636$$
$$209^2 = (218)(200) + 9^2 = 43{,}600 + 81 = 43{,}681$$

Remember that this method is exact for any number you can handle. A simple proof is shown as follows. Try this for a short cut in the future.

Here's how it works. Sometimes a shortcut for squaring numbers is easily explained by elementary algebra. Such explanations, often give great insight into the details of the method. To use algebra will help you recall the logic behind the method and show you how to proceed in a similar situation.

Let the number to be squared be equal to N, and the number of units above or below N be equal to a. On the left we show the algebraic steps in order. On the right the numerical equivalents from a previous example. Let $N = 87$ and $a = 13$.

Algebraic steps	Numerical example (N = 87)
$(N - a)(N + a) = (N^2 - a^2)$	$(87 - 13)(87 + 13) = 7400$
Add a^2 to step1.	Add 13 x 13 = 169
$(N^2 - a^2) + (a^2) = N^2$ = answer	7400 + 169 = 7569
	$= 87^2$

This derivation shows that the method is perfectly general and applies to any number N and to any difference a. The only limitation is the ability of the person doing the mental calculation. That is why we confine the discussion to two-digit numbers.

Of course, our aim was to simplify the work by choosing a so that one of the multipliers was a simple multiple of 10. In the first example

$$N = 18, a = 2, (N + a) = 20$$

As for the second example

$$N = 43, a = 3, (N - a) = 40, \text{etc.}$$

The simplest multiple of 10 need not be the lowest multiple of 10, as was shown earlier.

The answer is c) 221

To Review Some Basics

1. Addition and multiplication demonstrate the principle of commutative law.
a + b = b + a, or 5 + 8 = 8 + 5 = 13;
a x b = b x a = 3 x 4 = 4 x 3 = 12.

2. Subtraction is the inverse of addition:
if x – y = z, therefore y + z = x
or, 9 – 5 = 4, then 5 = 4 = 9.

3. Division is the inverse of multiplication:
if x ÷ y = z, then y x z = x
so, 63 ÷ 9 = 7, therefore 9 x 7 = 63.

ORDER OF OPERATIONS

TALKING ABOUT BASICS: $(3 + 2) + (3 \times 2) + 4 - 3 \div 3 \times 2 - 2 = ?$ To compute or calculate some upcoming exercises, remember this statement: **Rules of Operations.**

(Brackets First), Multiplications and Divisions (from left to right), Additions and subtractions (from left to right).

Calculate this: $(7 + 2 \times 3)(20 - 12 \div 4) = ?$: a) 136; b) 54; c) 221.

The answer is back on page 2.8

Got a Deck of Cards?

Take a deck of cards, leave out Jokers. All cards have a value, 1 to 10. But the Jack's value is now 1, Queen's is 2, and the King's is 3. Start turning the cards face up from the deck, and as you count, **each time you reach the sum of 10, your 10 register of points reverts to zero.** Eg., 4 + 3 = 7 + 4 = 11, (mentally 11 – 10 = 1), 1 + J (1) = 2 + Q (2) = 4 + 8 = 12 (think 2) + 8 = 10 (think 0), etc.,until you run out of cards. **Remainder: 4?** Keep this counting up, whenever you're bored. ***Good addition exercise!***

There's method in this madness. What you've been doing is an exercise and an introduction to a snappy card trick. Turn to page 13.8, please! *Learn this one and you'll have audiences!*

Take a look at these odd squares

From place to place in this book, we put a weird pattern of numbers. For example try this one on for size.

$$34^2 = 1156 \qquad 67^2 = 4489$$
$$334^2 = 111556 \qquad 667^2 = 444889$$
$$3334^2 = 11115556 \qquad 6667^2 = 44448889$$
$$33334^2 = 1111155556 \qquad 66667^2 = 4444488889$$

and so on and on. Now look here! Try this one on for size!

5,363,222,357 x 2,071,721 = 11,111,111,111,111,111.

What devious reasoning makes these two numbers equal all those ones? Anyone got an idea as to this phenomenon?

When we fool around with the number nine (9), we can have a field day! For instance 9 x 9 = 81. So what's new? Funny you should ask!

9 x 9 = 81
99 x 9 = 891
999 x 9 = 8991
9999 x 9 = 89991
99999 x 9 = 899991
and so on.
(note: always less one 9 than the multiplicand, but the first and last numbers make a total of 9)

Suppose we attempt to multiply by 99 and see wha' happens!

99 x 99 = 9801
999 x 99 = 98901
9999 x 99= 989901
99999 x 99 = 9899901
999999 x 99 = 98999901

Try the next one: 9999999 x 99 = ? You have the cadence or rhythm. Figure that one for yourself! It's always two 9's less that the multiplicand.

Should anyone ask you to square 9, or any 9 group, all the way up to 99999 x 99999, look at them coolly, and say:

9 x 9 = 81
99 x 99 = 9801
999 x 999 = 998001
9999 x 9999 = 99980001
99999 x 99999 = 9999800001

plus , if necessary 999999 x 999999 = 999998000001

I don't think that they'll bother you again! Except maybe to ask you how you learned to do all these terrific mental magic tricks!

"By Gar! How's is this happen to moi!"

An immigrant from somewhere in Europe came off the aircraft and started to walk through the terminal. He was almost penniless. He had a job to go to, but his cash had run out buying tax-free presents for his relatives. He looked at his last $10 bill and groaned about his poverty.

Suddenly, on the ground ahead he spied a crisp $5 bill. Happily, he picked it up, and a thought flashed through his mind: "Sacré blue!", said the immigrant from somewhere overseas, "my fortune has increased by 50 pourcent!", as he placed it in his coat pocket.

But alas, that pocket had a hole in it that had not been mended. When he hitched a ride to take him to his uncle's house, he was about to offer his new friend a tip, but the driver said "no thanks!". His hand was still in his pocket searching for the $5 bill but it was gone. Out through the unmended hole.

"Nom de Plume! Quelle despaire!" said the farmer from you-know-where: "But that is not to glum! Earlier, my fortune had been increase-ed by 50 pourcent, and now it has been decrease-ed by only 33 pourcent, mon dew! I am still, what you say, ahead by 17 pourcent, n'est-paw!"

– –

SOMETIMES I JUST HAVE TO HELP THEM COME TO TERMS WITH ADDING, SUBTRACTING, DIVIDING, MULTIPLYING, SQUARE ROOTS... CUBE ROOTS...

Chapter 3

COMING TO TERMS WITH MATH-E-MAGICS!

SUPER MATH-E-MAGICS takes it for granted that the youngest student reading this Course Book is in Grades 5 or 6. Conversely, the rest of you must be in high school, college, university and/or have been away from textbooks for quite a while and have perhaps forgotten, not but completely, the basic terms.

From the earliest introduction to Arithmetic, we have all learned to add or "plus" (addition), take away from, minus or subtract (subtraction), times-ing (multiplication), and "goes-into" (division).

We were also taught to call any number from zero (0) to nine (9), "Digits". These are all individual numbers, and there are ten (10) of them. The numbers follow: 1, 2, 3, 4, 5, 6, 7, 8, 9, 0. Not a big deal, but we'll start from there. By combinations, we can create any amounts of numbers: hundreds, thousands, millions, up to mega, giga, and other unpronounceable ones.

Place a number on each side of a slash (/) or oblique and we call those figures *Fractions*. 1/2, one half, 1/3, a third, 15/16, fifteen-sixteenths, and so on. A Fraction relates to a part of a whole number. The number on the left of the slash, or sometimes the one on top, is called the *Numerator* (it says how many parts of the lower number). Example: **2**/3 indicates two parts of the total unit. **3/3** represents the whole of the lower number called the *Denominator,* and 3/3 equal the value of 1.

As we get on into the Course, we will define the rest of the Terms: *Decimals* (4.506), *Percentages* (33%), *Ratios* (4:1), *Square Root* (what number multiplied by itself equals this number. [Eg.: $\sqrt{81} = 9$. ($9 \times 9 = 81$)]. *Cube Root* (what same number multiplied three times equals the number given. [Eg.: $\sqrt[3]{125} = 5$. ($5 \times 5 \times 5 = 125$)]. *Squaring* (number is multiplied by itself. ($8^2 = 8 \times 8 = 64$), *Cubing* (number multiplied by itself three times, thus ($7 \times 7 \times 7$ = Ans. 343), *Multiplication, Division, Powers of Infinite Length, etc.* So please be patient.

You must be in tune with each problem as we present them. We ask you to dig your heels in and be steadfast. Have the terminology handy, memorize everything until it becomes second nature. **The Rote Method** – keep repeating the rules until theory is as familiar as your own name. That way you will understand the new concepts we will be demonstrating. If the words we use are sometimes strange to your ears, get that old dictionary out and look it up.

- Let's take a short break here. ***Magic Reckoning:***

Take your house number and double it. Add 5. Multiply sum by 50 (Short Cut 5, Chapter 22.1, add two zeros and divide by 2) and then add you age, (if you're over 100, have your dad do it for you!). Add the number of days in a year, and subtract 615 from total sum. Lo, and behold, the last 2 figures are your age, the others will be your house address number. Try this out until it becomes rote in your mind, and then swing this on your pals.

In preparation for harder work to come, Short Cuts will be introduced in many hidden spots. Look for them. They're fascinating, and also very entertaining, especially if you're planning a life on the stage as a high-speed mental calculator! (Or a Banker!)

Have you ever tried Speed Reading? Sure helps with homework. Another thing to help your memory. **Quiet music**, preferably Classical. You don't have to like it, but it ain't stressful. Try it. Your math marks will be higher!

Motivational Thoughts for the Super Math-e-Magician:

JUST BECAUSE THEY SAY YOU CAN'T SUCCEED, DOESN'T MEAN OR PROVE YOU CAN'T!

GUESS WHAT?

We're 90% Illiterate and 95% Innumerate!

ITEM: The average high school graduate should have a vocabulary in the range of 14,000 to 20,000, University grads push that figure up to about 29,000 to 33,000, and scientists, professors, doctors, physicists and those in the semi-genius class push 50,000 to 65,000 words, and they all know the meanings of those words. Add several languages to which you claim familiarity, and the total becomes mind-boggling. So please use that dictionary. Intelligence is accumulated. You're only born with basic instincts. The rest of the life-time learning process depends on your attitude, wisdom, drive, and your own personal hype and motivation.

Mathematics and Magic go hand in hand. To revel in the art of magic, to conjure up shapes and images in one's mind is the penultimate joy of entertainment. Leave your troubles behind and let your mind wander to strange formulae and suspense.

Never let it be said that you weren't ambitious, interesting, or worthy of wonderful ideas. Rather, let them say of you, "What a fascinating mind! Never really seems at a loss for an idea, or a solution. On top of that, amazingly intelligent. What a lovely person!"

We heartedly recommend that you read Chapter 7 at this point!

That low man goes on adding one to one,
His hundred's soon hit;
This high man, aiming at a million,
Misses a unit.

(Browning)

SORRY... BUT THE PURPOSE OF THIS BOOK IS TO USE THAT THING YOU CALL A BRAIN... SO NO CALCULATORS!

Chapter 4

Computing Mentally – Short Cuts

Many problems can be and should be solved by mental computation. (Using the brain, for instance.) Mental computing is a practical life skill that must receive increased emphasis in the mathematical process or program.

Mental Computation Strategies for Addition and Subtraction

There are many ways of resolving addition and subtraction problems mentally. **Short Cut Examples:**

54 + 39 = ??	67 + 48 = ??	348 + 74 = ???
50 + 39 = 89	60 + 40 = 100	300 + 70 = 370
89 + 4 = 93	7 + 8 = 15	370 + 40 + (8 + 4) =
	100 + 15 = 115	410 + 12 = 422
34 + 29 + 66 =	35 + 70 + 95 =	774 – 489 =
34 + 30 – 1 = 63	35 + 70 = 105	774 – 500 = 274
63 + 66 = 129	105 + 95 = 200	274 – 11 = 263

Did you notice: 774 + 489 = 1,263 (1000 more than the answer)? It wasn't intentional!

Similar Short Cut Strategies Are Used for Multiplication:

3 x 36 = 3 x 30 = 90 + (3 x 6 =) 18 = 108;
5 x 67 = 5 x 60 = 300 + (5 x 7 =) 35 + 300 = 335, and so on.

As we open the door to Short Cuts, don't be amazed that things will seem so easy. Your grasp of the techniques will grow with every turn of the page and each and every completed Exercise. So bear with us as we open the Path to Mystical Short Cuts!

Meet TABLE 1:

A	B	C	D	E	F	G	H	I	J	K	L
94	87	80	73	66	59	52	45	38	31	24	17
10	3	96	89	82	75	68	61	54	47	40	33
26	19	12	98	5	84	91	70	77	56	63	49
42	28	35	14	21	93	86	72	79	58	51	65
44	37	30	23	9	16	95	81	88	74	67	60
46	53	32	39	25	18	11	4	97	83	90	76
69	62	55	48	41	34	20	27	13	6	99	92
85	71	78	64	57	50	36	43	29	22	8	15

We hope that our explanations from here on in will be accepted as both realistically in keeping with academic rules of learning as well as being fun, interesting, creating amazement and amusement both for yourself, your audiences, your friends, teachers, and especially, and above all, your parents.

They deserve the best from you. They have put their hearts and souls into you. Go that extra effort and get an excellent education, and reap the profits that only concentration, dedication and will-power can achieve for you.

If you don't know, ask questions. If you can't do it, try again and again. Success is for those who overcome their fear and climb that supposedly insurmountable hill, the cliffs of your own imagination.

So you slip a little. Big deal! Two forward, one back, still does get to the top!!

Progress comes with habits. Dig your feet in and say, "I CAN DO IT!" And you will do it!. Try it, you'll like yourself in the mirror, and in other people's eyes and hearts. Good luck!

Motivational Thoughts for the Super Math-e-Magician:

IF YOU THINK YOU CAN OR CANNOT BECOME SUCCESSFUL, YOU WILL ALWAYS BE RIGHT!

Let's Introduce You to Short Cuts!

First, take a pencil, pen, but, please, no calculators within reach. Lots of blank paper. Radio off or according to your concentration level, or attention span. Let's understand these ground rules right from the start. If you don't understand the problem, then start over again at the last spot where you did understand.

It takes time to set up a pattern of remembering. "I told him/her and I told him/her! (I've got to remember these gender changes or I'm in real trouble from some activist crowd!) "Finally s/he got it right!" Sounds familiar? So says your parent, teacher, etc.

Ready?

Let's go. Given this problem: Multiply 26 by 26. Or perhaps try 26 x 22? You are requested to look at it and write the answer down. "Ah! C"mon! You're kidding, aren't you?" Fear not, we have a method, a very easy one. Turn to: "Up Some. . . Down Some", Chapter 2.4. Or Our Boomerangs, Chapter 5.1, **Stage 3**.)

This book of MATH-E-MAGICS is geared for that kind of operation. If we ask you **"What's the square of 69^2**, then you must write down that figure without any written calculations visible. **No calculator, no step-by-step procession of worked-out stream of figures; no draw a line, no add vertically, right to left.** That's finished from now on.

So? 69 squared? What's the answer? The Right Answer is 4761.

" OK, let's start these short cuts right now. "

When we say do it mentally, we mean **think!, think!, think!**. It's a difficult thing to stray away from the TV. Some friends call and you're out the door, gone. Well, this course is apt to follow with you. Everything about the SUPER MATH-E-MAGICS book is fun, pure clear brain waves. Stun your friends with your new trade. ***Stage Calculator-in-training.*** It is a fact. You'll be a whiz! Believe in yourself! You're half way there!

When we use a Short Cut for Squaring, refer to Chapter 20.

This works well when the problem contains small squares in its solving.

67	43	89
<u>67</u>	<u>43</u>	<u>79</u>
4489	1849	7031

On left side, 67 x 67, think 7^2 –> 49, write 9, mentally carry 4; 6 + 6 = 12 x upper units 7= 84, + 4 remainder (rem.) = 88, write 8, carry 8; finally 6 x 6, or 6^2, 36 + 8 = 44. That's it. Your answer is 4489. Similarly, 43^2 becomes 1849. The last only varies in this method as it is not a square, but gets a bit ponderous when 7 + 8 = 15 x 9 = 135 + 8 = 143, write 3; 7 x 8 = 56 + 14, giving 70 to whole answer 7031.

Another short cut for squares ending in 9, such as 49 x 49 steps this way: Go one unit higher than the 9, making the square of 50. That's easy enough, 2500. Piece of cake!

Get the sum of number 49, plus 1 higher = 49 + 50 = 99. Now take 99 from 2500, (2500 – 99 = 2401. The right answer.

Boomerangs in Chapter 5, Stage 3 offers a much easier solution. So hang in there, let your mind soak in these different ways to compute.

Certain squaring or multiplying numbers that have small differences are quickly resolved by the following methods:

45 x 46 –> square smaller and add smaller number. 45 x 45 = 2025 + 45 = 2,070.
27 x 26 –> square larger; and subtract larger number: 27 x 27 = 729 – 27 = 702.
Or square smaller 26 x 26 = (676), add the smaller = 702.

31 x 29 = 30 x 30 = 900; – 1 = 899. Average squared minus 1.
43 x 45 = 44 x 44 = 1936; – 1 = 1935.

34 x 31 = 1054
When the difference is 3, add 1 to smaller number, and square; 31 + 1 = 32^2 = 1024. Subtract 1 from smaller number (31 – 1 = 30) and add to 1024 = 1054. (ans.)

46 x 42 = 1932
Should there be a difference of 4, add 2 to smaller, or subtract 2 from greater (average), and square sum (44^2) = 1936. Subtract square of 2 to this partial answer. 1936 – 4 = 1932
Another explanation: Square average less 4.

38 x 32 = 1216.
Same as above. Square mean average of both numbers less 9.
38 + 32 = 70 ÷ 2 = 35^2 = 3 x (3 + 1 = 4) = 12 25, less 9 = 1216.

Short Cuts (see Chapter 22) list over 100 such methods for fast and accurate answers.

Please bear with the author and practise all the variables in this book. Certainly there are other methods to divide, multiply, add or subtract, but why not learn to train the Brain to ponder devious and magical twists of the imagination. Those who don't think, stay static. Those who dream the impossible create the future we so wish.

Another twist to rapid calculation is one that should catch on. Try this on your friends for speed.

When two numbers in the tens area, say, 16 and 14, whose units digits add to 10 are to multiplied, do this:

16 x 14 = (multiply 6 x 4 = 24, and shove another 2 up front. Your answer is quickly visible + 224. Look at these numbers:
19 x 11 = 209 (the 0 is placed between)

17 x 13 = 221
18 x 12 = 216
15 x 15 = 225

There are great short cuts to come. Practise, think, remember!

ANOTHER MASTERPIECE!
16 +
12 x
THE LENAGHAN BOOMERANG

Chapter 5

BOOM-E-RANGS! – Stage 1

16 times 12? Let's take a TUTOR Short Cut. This new technique has never been used before. And it's called "***the Lenaghan Tutor Boomerang***"!

1 9 +
1 8 x

As you can see, I've drawn a boomerang around the 16 and the 2 only. That's where the action is. I only use **+** and **x** in the following short cut.

19 **+** 8 = 27. (Remember from now on, you will always place a **zero** (**0**) after that first calculation. Those figures read **270**. That's half the deal. Multiply 9 **x** 8 and you get **72**. Second half finished. Join **270** + **70 + 2** = **342**. Simple as all that!

No more memorizing endless tables of 13 times, 14 times, 16 times. Just look at the top number, add the units figure below it, stick on a zero, multiply vertically the units figures, add both results and Voil`a!

Do you see the logical progression of answers flashing before you: **18 x 17** = ??? 18 + 7 equals 25 (plus zero) = **250**. 8 x 7 = **56**. Take **250** plus **50 + 6.** You immediately get **306** (mentally). 18 x 18 = **26(0)** + **64** = **324**; 19 x 19 = 28(0) + 81 = 361.

Present world-wide school methods use 16 x 12 = 16(0) + (16 x 2) 32 = 192. Right answer, but for speed try 19 x 18 that same way. Suddenly you're dealing with a very cumbersome 19 x 18 = **19(0)** + 19 x 8 = (9 x 8 = 72) **2**, carry 7 –(8 x 1 = 8) + 7= **152.** 190 + 152 (ponderous) = adding down = **342**. –> ***Slower!***

I challenge the older method with this new system!

Swish, faster than a speeding bullet. No more zeros on your math reports. When speed and accuracy counts – ***TUTOR BOOMERANG it!***

I want you to try the following series of multiplication using the Tutor ***Boomerang Method: STAGE 1 !!***

Exercise 4

19 x 14 = ; 16 x 18 = ; 17 x 19 = ; 15 x 12 = ; 16 x 11 = ;

17 x 12 = ; 14 x 14 = ; 18 x 15 = ; 16 x 16 = ; 19 x 19 = ;

12 x 12 = ; 17 x 17 = ; 16 x 14 = ; 15 x 12 = ; 19 x 13 = ;

13 x 17 = ; 16 x 19 = ; 17 x 14 = ; 13 x 13 = ; 18 x 18 = ;

This technique works for all numbers in the tens group. Practice your own combinations and bypass the old-fashioned way of memorizing long list of tables. From now on just look at mixed 2-number sets in that 11 to 19 group and relax. Using the Boomerang Method means no more rote. Mind you, rote is one of the best ways to commit poems, theatrical plots, etc., to easy recall. ***But the Boomerang is practical in many ways.***

You have successfully completed the **Stage 1** version of the Boom/Method. What about 20 x 19, or 24 x 17, or even 29 x 14? Try it the new way we showed you, and you'll fall flat on your face. "Hey! I can't get the right answers. Why won't it work?" Thought you'd never ask!

What you did with Tutor's Stage 1 didn't involve a different tens value. You went into the tens' mode only and now you're asked to meld tens into the higher tens' value (20s, 30s, 40s, etc.). Now things get better and more interesting. Let's explore further!

Ready for Stage 2?

Let's go. This time we use the 20 -level.

Example: 24 x 17 = (doing it the old way . . .)

7 times 24 equals 168;
and 1 times 24 equals 24.

168
24
408 (correct answer)

CAUTION! Using Stage 1, you get 24 + 7 = 31 (0)–> zero is understood here; then you multiply 4 x 7 = 28; so 310 + 28 = 338! "**hello**"– but that's nowhere near 408, which is the right answer, correct? The true answer is 408, and you're missing a value of 70. So what went wrong? That's where **the Tutor Boomerang Method, Stage 2,** differs from Stage 1.

STAGE 2 ... *(completely different!!)*

Note this. When you mess around with unlike levels of the Boomerang Method, you use the lower tens' value. I'll explain:

Earlier when you multiplied 19 times 14, the tens' value (1)9 and (1)4 were in a sense on the same floor. Now when we deal with the people upstairs on the second digit level. Capish? So we need a different language, sort of.

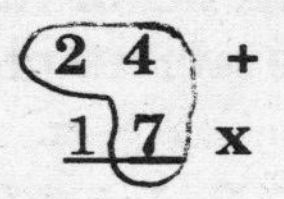

Before, at this point, we added 24 and 7, remembering to add (0), which now becomes 31(0); then we multiplied 4 times 7 vertically. Once again you can see, we've drawn a boomerang around the 24 and the 7. [24 + **7** = 31(0)] All we need now is another 98 points. OK, but where do we get it?

- New Second Rule here: 4 x 7 = 2 (**8**). **But this time we only use that 8!** *Keep your brain open.*

So what happens to 2 of 28? Think on that for a moment! (pause here for a moment, and don't look any farther into this section).

Go ahead, think on this. So far, the answer has only reached a total of 318. But the true answer is **408.** So? We're still missing 90, aren't we?

So why don't we just add the **2** of the 4 x 7 = (**2**)8 to the **7** of 1(**7**). Right! And we get our missing **9!** (We place the 9 in front of the 8 of 28, add it to the 310 and, *Bingo* . . . 408!) **That's how we raise our 98!**

At this crucial point in the answer, the answer is visible. First, we arrived at 310, then derived the units' 8, but lacked the tens' value. By adding the vertical multiplication of 4 x (7) = (2)8 – 2 plus the 7 of such figure, we come up with the 9 of 98. Ergo, 310 plus 98 = 408, the right answer to the problem. And this calculation has never been done before. This is something entirely new to Math.

All this is done in the blink of an eye or the twitch of your nose. **Short-Cut Number One**! Now this is really a mind-grabber!

Again I want to impress on you to try this series of multiplication using the Boomerang Method. It must be practised till it becomes second nature to you, the old "ROTE METHOD. Let's try out a few examples:

29 x 14 = ; 26 x 12 = ; 28 x 19 = ; 22x 12 = ; 26 x 16 = ;

27 x 16 = ; 24 x 14 = ; 28 x 13 = ; 23 x 16 = ; 29 x 12 = ;

22 x 18 = ; 17 x 17 = ; 16 x 14 = ; 21 x 15 = ; 20 x 19 = ;

29 x 19 = ; 26 x 11 = ; 27 x 19 = ; 25 x 14 = ; 23 x 18 = .

(Answers at end of book)

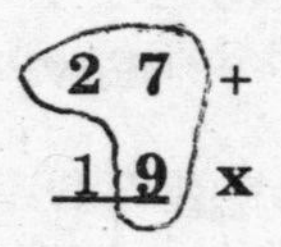

This technique works well if you remember that last crucial motion. In the Boomerang Method, if you get, say, 27 + 9 = 36(0), then 7 **x** 9 = **63,** the **6** of that (**6**)3 is added to the 9 to make up the tens value, namely **6 + 9 = 15**(3). The correct answer, 360 + 153 = **513**. ***Keep at it, until you understand it!***

• Note here , please: There will be a shifting of logic in the manner in which you might find the solutions for the coming Tutor Boomerang Methods. It must be understood that the varying techniques propounded in this course in no way counteract the present academic methods taught in schools. Rather, it demonstrates that no current methods used in academic regions are gospel. There are many roads to Damascus. Let the light fall where it may. In such case, here's a lot more short (?) cuts.

STAGE 1: To date, you have learned to multiply between 10 and 20.

e.g.: To obtain the product of:
18 x 12 = (you mentally calculated: 18 + 2 = 20 tens
8 x 2 = 16, getting a product of 20 tens plus 16 = 216.

STAGE 2: Then we showed you how to speed calculate numbers mixed of twenty status and tens (mixed levels):

e.g.: To obtain the product of 27 x 19:

27 + 1(9) = (mentally) 27 + 9 = 36(0), then 7 x 9 = 63. The 3 of 63 is added to 360, giving a partial answer of 363. The 6 of that (6)3 is then added to the 9 to make up the tens value, namely 6 + 9 = 15(3). 15(0) + 3 = 153.
The correct answer is 360 + 153 = 513.

STAGE 3

Moving forward to a new higher level, multiplying two numbers of which the tens are similar:

(Simplified, you add to one units number the units of the other, and multiply this sum by the figure of the lower tens. I hope that explains it. Then to the product of the tens, add the product of the units. You don't get it, do you? O.K.!)

e.g.: 48 x 43 – (as in Stage 1) –> 48 + **3** of 4(**3**), remember?
Calculate mentally, of course: 48 + 3 = 51.
51 x 4 of (**4**)3 = 204 tens, or 204(0)
8 x 3 = 24
Product : 2040 + 24 = 2,064. There now, that didn't hurt, did it?

Let's try a second go at it: 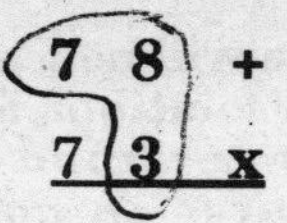

First the product of 78 x 73 (again mentally, always mentally)

78 x 73 = **78** + (7)**3** = 81; **81 x 7 (**of **73)** = 567 tens, or 567(0);
2nd move – 8 x 3 = 24 –> therefore 5670 + 24 = **5,694.** Check!
Or try the **Up Some/Down Some** method.

When calculating the products of tens in the ninety range, the procedure shifts slightly.

For example: 98 x 96.
e.g., (mentally) 98 + 6 = 104 x 9 (of **96)** = or 936 tens or 936(0)
8 x 6 = 48. Product: 9360 + 48 = **9,408**

Complex Complementary Multiplication

• **Complementary Multiplication could take place here:** When you are in the range of 100 and closely with 10 to 15 units each side, there is an alternate method such as:

To obtain the product of the same 98 x 96, but the complementary way is as follows:

Mentally calculate: 100 – 98 = 2
100 – 96 = 4
2 x 4 = 08

Subtract crossways, 98 – 4 = 94 and 96 – 2 = 94 (1st 2 digits)
Product required: 9,408.

Let's try one a little larger:

Find the product of 995 x 984:

As in 98 x 96, the complements were 2 and 6; now in this problem we can see the complements are 5 and 16. The method of multiplication is very easy and effective when the numbers are both near 100, or both near 1,000.

In order to multiply 995 and 984, first subtract the complements of either number from the other. The result is the same. The complement of 995 is 5, the complement of 984 is 16, when cross-subtracted, the results are the same = 979. the rest is easier – 16 x 5 = 80. You're nearly finished. In multiplying two-digit numbers and also three-digit numbers, such as 995 x 984, always insert one extra digit and another when needed to make it complete to a four-digit or six-digit number – in this case, a six-digit – it is zero.

```
  98          995
x 96        x 984
9408       979080
```

Here are two more examples of plus and minus complements: This calls for some deep thinking here. This is not an easy one at first, but re-read this and you'll see light in the tunnel.

$$\begin{array}{ll} 985 & 15 \\ 97 & 3 \end{array} \qquad \begin{array}{ll} 9968 & 32 \\ 103 & \bar{3} \end{array}$$

In the first of these, we have written the thousand-complement of the upper number and the hundred-complement of the lower number. When we do our diagonal subtraction, we have to take into account that there is a factor of ten between 1000 and 100. So we obtain the highest three digits of the required product either by subtracting 30 from 985, or by subtracting 15 from 970. In either case we get 955. We now multiply 15 by 3, giving us 45. The final product can therefore be written immediately as 955 45.

In the second example, we have written the ten-thousand-complement of the upper number and the hundred complement of the lower number. In the latter case, however, 103 is greater than 100 and its complement therefore negative. We have only to indicate this by writing a bar over the 3. This time, the diagonal subtraction has to take into account the factor of one-hundred between 10000 and 100. We first either subtract 32 from 10300, or we add 300 to 9968 Adding 300 is, of course, equivalent to subtracting minus 3 x 100. In either case we will obtain 10268. We now multiply 32 by –3, giving us –96. Writing what we have obtained so far gives:

$$\begin{array}{ccc} 9968 & & 32 \\ \underline{103} & \times & \underline{\bar{3}} \\ 10268 & & \overline{96} \end{array}$$

We write the bar over the $\bar{3}$ and $\overline{96}$ to indicate that these are minus quantities. Subtracting 96 is equivalent to adding 4 and then subtracting 100. We therefore write 04 in place of 96, and subtract 1 from 8, to give us the final product, which we can now write as 1026704.

We hope this gives you some neat satisfaction to absorb this information. *Who said math isn't fun? Well, some of it is.*

Here We Step into the Big Time

Stepping up the width and breadth of the Boomerang, let's tie up the eyes on this. Let's multiply 59 x 57 for a refresher.

Using the Boomerang process, we think 59 + 7 = 66. No sweat! But under the old rules we multiplied vertically and got out in one step. Well, my readers, this time we don't. That 66 has to undergo a violent mark-up. Now we're in the 50's level. So we multiply by 5. We now have 66 x 5 = 330, we still think 330(0), right. Vertically for step 2, (9 x 7 = 63). So far everything is normal. Results to date – 3300 + 63 = **3363**. This time it's the right answer.

This method works well with all identical levels to 99 x 99.

Now to encompass the variables that arise between the war of the different tens' levels.

When the varied levels of tens are brought into the Boomerang Technique, again we meet with change. But a vast change is immediately noticed. **Pay attention – this is brand new.**

Multiply 68 x 32. The old fashioned school way seems quite very simple. We think 2 x 8 = 16, write 6, carry 1; 2 x 6 = 12 + 1 =13. Top line now reads 136. Second line, slightly left, 3 x 8 = 24, write 4, carry 2; 3 x 6 = 18 + 2 = 20. add top line 136

add lower line 204

answer: 2176

STAGE 4: *Biggest Boomerang Method*

Multiply 68 x 32 (**ans. 2176**). We'll let you see the answer first.

68 + 2 = 70. Right on track, old method. (see Chap. 5.6) **We have a multiplier with a value of 3 tens.** So let's multiply 70 x 3 = 210 and we naturally now think 210(0). **Next step gets involved.** Remember we need 76 to arrive at right answer. We now multiply vertically – (using the old method we would have 16 as our adding for the final result). ***But, oh no, there's still a few more steps. We did say this was a new method!***

When you multiply top right to bottom this time: 8 x 2 = **16,** only use the **6**. Right off the bat, let's tell you what happens next. You will notice **that there is a difference between the 60 level and the 30 level.** So with that difference of 3 in mind, we then multiply the **3 x 2** (of **32**) = **6 + 1** (16 of the vertical reckoning) = **7 (we just found the tens' section of the final answer: 76.** Combined parts give the answer: **2176.**

Hope you're still with me. Because I've got some exercises for you to try out.

STAGE FOUR EXERCISE

1. 87 x 46	4. 53 x 28	7. 87 x 49	10. 65 x 45
2. 97 x 48	5. 79 x 41	8. 96 x 87	11. 63 x 23
3. 84 x 43	6. 51 x 41	9. 72 x 36	12. 103 x 43

Careful now! There's a catch in one of these!

Supplementary Multiplication

Supplementary Multiplication can also be done as long as the numbers to be multiplied are not to difficult or mind-disturbing.

Example: Find the product of 106 x 103.

106 – 100 = 6
103 – 100 = 3

(When above 100, instead of subtracting, add crossways or crosswise.)

103 + 6 or 106 + 3 = 109 (hundreds value, this time) – 10900.
Follow the normal units multiplying, 6 x 3 = 18.

Product required: 10900 + 18 = 10,918.

To take on four-digit numbers, there is a slight variance in our technique.

Problem:

Find product of 1006 x 1002 by the Supplementary Method of Multiplication:

108	1006
x 103	x 1002

This time we have supplements in excess of 100 and also 1,000. The supplements of 108 and 103 are 8 and 3, while with 1006 and 1002, they are 6 and 2. As before it is quite easy. 108 x 103 is a repeat of ordinary supplement multiplication. 108 + 3 = 111, and the product of 8 x 3 = 24, answer 11124.

108	1006
x 103	x 1002
11124	1008012

In cases of figures in the 1000's range, remember that extra cipher (0) that has to be inserted. It is sometimes necessary to insert as many as two extra zeros so that the product will correctly have seven digits in the right answer.

• Around about here, let's just look at the multiplying of **two numbers ending in the same figure or units' value.**

To obtain the product of: 94
(calculate mentally): x 64

9 x 6 = 54 hundreds
9 + 6 = 15
15 x 4 = 60 tens
54 hundreds + 60 tens = 600 tens
4 x 4 = 16

Product required:
600 tens + 16 = 6016. answer

At this point, let's return to some exercises of the brain. Chapter 4.2, Table 1: Add 14 to all column C figures; multiply each by 36.

There is another way to multiply any combination of two figured numbers, regardless of their having a common tens or common units.

For example: Find the product of 87 x 38.

Using the Boomerang Method, 87 + 8 = 95. Calculate mentally: 95 x 3 = 285 tens or 2850. As usual, it's the same to here. But?

Multiply top right to bottom this time: 7 x 8 = **56,** just use the **6**. You will notice that there is a **level difference of 5** between the 80 level and the 30 level. So with that **difference of 5** in mind, we then multiply the **5** x **8** (of 3**8**) = **40** + **5** (56 of the vertical units reckoning) = **45 tens.** 2850 + 450 + 6 = **3,306.** Now if you can do it faster, you can make a name for yourself.

Here's some thing that's just a little weirder!

Half Complementary Multiplication

When you doodle with math, you get some strange urges to be different from the rest. Why not do it this way or reverse the whole order of accepted techniques. Some will say "Don't mess with Mother Math!" Well, I did just a few months ago, September/93, it was just a fluke. An abberation, sort of.

It goes like this: Complementary multiplication reaches an acceptable method of multiplying number adjacent to 100 or 1,000. What if?. . . What if you took any figure, say 96, for instance, and tried to multiply it by 47, using that same method on p. 4.6 of this Chapter. The logic I thought I would use first was divide the 100 by 2. Therefore all numbers would be treated as the original rule, but that didn't work. So, what's left as an alternate? So back to multiplying 96 x 47 = 4512.

The outcome of several failures started to show a pattern, a continuity appeared. When I reached one level or plateau of nearly the right answer, I subtracted from the real answer the figures that I was then getting.

Let me explain, 96, using the Complementary Method (C/M from now on), gave a difference of 4 from 100. Conversely, 47 (1/2-CM) gave a difference of 3 from 50. (At this point I thought I was working at half speed.) Anyway, 4 x 3 = 12. At least I got that right. And 12 was part of the right answer. Now all I had to do was raise 4500 from some where. (I didn't have a number account in Switzerland bank! Dry humour here!!)

Remember our two modes (CM) and (1/2-CM) -> 100 – 96 = 4 and (half a hundred) 50 – 47 = 3.

Also recollect that the criss-cross results are:

96 ╲╱ 4
47 ╱╲ 3

1st New Rule: 96 minus 3, 47 minus 4, giving us 93 and 43. One half of 93 is 46.50, and we leave 43 as being 43.00. So it followed that the **4500** that I was looking for was just a step or two away. But from what angle? From the answer 4512 less 12 which I had attained by multiplying the differences from 100 and 50, I needed a clean 200 value from somewhere to add to 4300. But how and from which twisted number action? So I put it away for a while. A week or two later I picked up the same threads of reasoning and suddenly a quirk of logic showed up.

On reviewing, I noticed that the difference between 96 and 47 was in the range of 50 apart, not approximately 60, but approximately 50. So what figure somewhere in my calculations rested a number that when multiplied by 50 would give me 200. By now you guessed it!

The complement of 96 – the lonely 4.

50 x 4 = 200 – > 4300 + 200 + 12 = 4512.
QED!!! Gotcha!!

Relief, relax, and try a few more, and I did. They all worked. So, dear reader, I don't know whether or not I've created a friend or a monster – but this I do know. I've come across another way to confuse pupils, and others, in more than one way to calculate without a Calculator. Use your mind! Crank it up and see how far you can go; see how far it can take you!

So what do we do now? I'll just have to say it's Lenaghan's Law. When you want to multiply a number higher than the 80's to a number above or below 50 within a respectable range of, say, 20, it will work in three motions. Always remember to look for that difference in the tens' value between the two numbers. Difference and the criss-cross of the lower tens' value. So there you are.

There's been no earth-shaking feeling, but an independent glow as self-satisfaction in knowing that perhaps there are more ways to skin a cat. It doesn't necessarily follow that this technique should be called a Short Cut, but ain't it grand to feel you know something that no one else ever knew or did!

You younger people have the best chances in the world, what with the fast spin-off of geniuses in the ever-expanding computer markets and medical gene researching that are stretching our health horizons and brain levels onward and ever upward. Hang in there . . . the best is yet to come!

Try working these out, just for the heck of it. This exercise will give you a twist away from school math, and perhaps start you into a better number sense.

EXERCISE 5

1. 88 x 46   4. 93 x 42   7. 87 x 44   10. 95 x 45
2. 93 x 48   5. 89 x 49   8. 96 x 83   11. 93 x 73
3. 94 x 44   6. 91 x 41   9. 92 x 30   12. 93 x 63

Careful now! There's a catch in one of them!

By the way, this treatment also works above 100 and also above 50. See if you can spot the odd difficulty. Good Luck!!

• *Here's a Task I set myself* •

Question? A novel way to use the Boomerang, over 100!
This is what it came out as: Compute 158 x 144.

Solution: 158 – 100 = 58
144 – 100 = 44

144 + 58 or 158 + 44 = **202(00)** Boomerang/Supplementary
(58 + 2) x (44 – 2) = 42 x 60 = **2520** (Up some/Down some)
5**8** x 4**4** = 8 x 4 = **32** (units digits only)
2520 + 32 = (2520 + 30 = 2550 + 2) = **2552**
20200 + 2552 = **22,752** – incidentally the right answer!

Another way to multiply two numbers!

"Boy, Do Odd Numbers Act Strange!"

Think of any three digits (abc). Repeat same digits (abcabc). Now you have a whole number that's not doing very much. You look at it; it looks at you. Big deal! Ah-ha! Enter from the wings come a troop of fresh unsullied and perky numbers. Introducing the executioners, meet 7, 11, 13, 77, 91, 143, 1001! (I think I've seen these guys somewhere before.)

Let's say that the original number was 648. Then we copied it one more time, making it 648,648.

They line up and raising their sharp edges start taking pot-shots at the double number. Quickly they shred the formidable 6-digit whole number into a whimpering threesome. But take another look. Well, I'll be! It's the original three-digits we started with a few moment earlier. "Wha' happ'n?"

When we wrote abc, then doubled it again as *abc,abc,* in reality the position values for this series was: 100,000a + 10,000b + 1,000c + 100a + 10b + c = 100,100a + 10,010b + 1,001c. Please note that 13 x 11 x 7 = 1,001. By trial, you will find that these numbers are factors of 100,100, 10,010 and 1,001. Ergo, you're capable of dividing these figures into *abcabc*. Now if you combine these numbers into other numbers, you get results such as: 77, 91, 143, 1,001.

Let's experiment: Take 648,648, and rip it apart with first, 7, then 11, followed by 13, 77, 91, 143, and lastly, 1,001.

648,648 ÷ 7 = 92,664
648,648 ÷ 11 = 58,968
648,648 ÷ 13 = 49,896
648,648 ÷ 77 = 8,424
648,648 ÷ 91 = 7,128
648,648 ÷ 143 = 4,536
648,648 ÷ 1,001 = 648

Give this a good long look. The more you study speed math, the greater your enthusiasm for new horizons, newer short cuts.

...AND NOW WE HAVE A MOTHER DAUGHTER TEAM READY TO PLAY OUR FAVORITE NUMBER GAME MAGIC SQUARES

Chapter 6
MAGIC SQUARES

Here's something for the stage, or perhaps a party or your own classroom. Ask for a number from your audience. As an afterthought, ask for a number, say, between 40 and 100. (This number is placed at the edge of the blackboard, or whatever medium you use for attention .

Draw a large square. Draw five lines vertically, and the five lines horizontally. "Hey, look, 16 small squares!" You now explain to your captivated audience that you're going to take their offered number, which in this instance, was 59, and place in these 16 squares numbers, which when added horizontally or diagonally, or even vertically, will always add up to 59. No matter what direction anybody adds it will always add up to 59. "And I will also recite a short stanza from Shakespeare, or whatever comes to mind, that's tolerable to you folks." "How about Gunga Din?"

By now you have figured out your starting number for the first square. 59 has already been broken down as you were drawing the square, as follows:

59 minus **30** (**the magic number always used** for the basis of this operation) = 29. Divide 29 by 4 = 7, with a remainder 1.

Put the result of the division into the square (uppermost right hand corner, which we will call "blank". (For your own use, here is a memory guide for this trick. Consider and in your practice of the trick, number off the squares from left to right, as follows:

1	2	3	4
5	6	7	8
9	10	11	12
13	14	15	16

Space Number **4** is "BLANK". The quotient 7 is written here. The sequence then starts: (These numbers shift in a specific design.) In space **6** (write 8), space 9 (write 9), in **15** write 10, **14** (11), (and so on, filling up the empty spaces) 12, 7, 1, 11, 13, 2, 8, **5, 3, 16, 10,** plus the blank = 16 spaces. **Remember the remainder - 1.** This 1 is added to **one** specific spot of certain squares: 3, **5,** 10, 16. Remainder makes each line add up to 59.

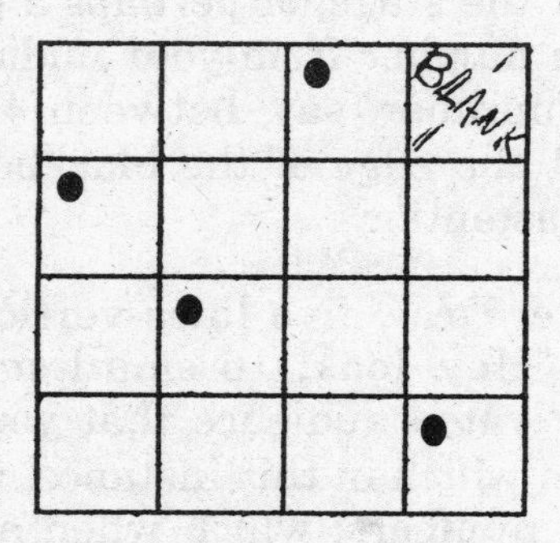

Below is a completely worked out square. Below 30 (the row total of the basic square) you would have to work in decimals, Steer away from anything lower than 30. Also above 100, it gets a little hard to check; but try it anyway. You can work comfortably in between 40 and 100. Most people suggest 60's to 80's. To prove out each columns is time-consuming. Take one each of several directions to prove the square, and then move to another trick of your choice. More math-conscious pals should be also told that the four centre squares also add to the magical process. You might also mention that there are over 30 ways to arrive at of total 59. Even the inner square equals 59.

14	**17**	**21**	**7**
20	**8**	**13**	**18**
9	**23**	**15**	**12**
16	**11**	**10**	**22**

Let's look into future work in this Book.

For your entertainment and perhaps an improvement of your math marks in school or work place, we have compiled an interesting assortment of short cuts.

You will be presented with an array of lightning mental motions. Practise these tests. Constant review of these formulae will sharpen your intelligence, and you'll be as keen and flexible as a rapier. Think, think, think. The more your brain is in motion, the longer the recall processes will work in your favor. Incidentally, the man who thinks, lives longer. Take a look at all the elderly scientific men in the world.

From page to page, we will ask you to add, subtract, divide, and multiply various up grades to Tables scattered throughout this Course. ***PENSA***, a new type of mental agility grader, will come in Chapter 10.

Don't jump about with the different Chapters. They will link up in quick time, if you persevere. Exercises to work will be highlighted.

Let's get back to work. We talked in the early stages of this MATH-E-MAGICS Book about doing Squares.

Boomerang will get you any square from 11 to 99. As you noticed 15 x 15 = 225. But also note that by simply increasing the figure 1 of 15, by 1, (1 + 1 = 2) and multiplying the result: 2 x 1 = 2 and adding 5 x 5 = 25, the answer is met. 15 x 15 = 225. Similarly, **35^2** = **3** x 4 (3 + **1** = 4) = 12 25, the 25 is understood to be a constant response to any number ending in a 5.

EXERCISE 6

Resolve the squares of the following numbers ending in 5.

25^2 ; 45^2 ; 75^2 ; 55^2 ; 95^2 ; 65^2 ; 15^2 ; 85^2 ; 125^2 ; 115^2 ; 105^2 ; 315^2 . Make up some tough ones for yourself.

Before we get too deeply into squares, cubes, 5th powers, some algebra, logarithms, etc., let's see what you can do with some addition and subtraction. OK, so do I. We all have to review before we climb higher. Addition, subtraction, division are the hand tools to Mathematical Structure. Call it the cement or bonding adhesive. But review we shall!

EXERCISE 7

Go to Table 1 on page Chap. 4.2. Column D, add 4 units value to every number in column until you reach 157, then reverse and subtract 7 from 157 until you reach 10. Were you right each way? If not give it another try.

Remember Page 5.14? Here's Another!

Question? Want a repeat of a novel way to use the Boomerang?

This is what it came out as –> Compute 163 x 146.
Solution: 163 – 100 = 63
146 – 100 = 46
163 + 46 or 146 + 63 = 209(00) Boomerang/Complementary
(63 x 46 = (cross multiplying – sometimes a fast way) = 2898
20900 + 2898 = **23,798** – the right answer!

Want to try another one? Compute 138 x 124!
Solution: 138 – 100 = 38
124 – 100 = 24
138 + 24 or 124 + 38 = 162(00) Boomerang/Supplementary
(38 + 2) x (24 – 2) = 22 x 40 = 880
3**8** x 2**4** = 8 x 4 = 32
880 + 32 = 912
16200 + 912 = **17,112** again the right answer!

Make up some samples for yourself!

Prime Time Comes in Chapter 8

In a few pages from now, Prime Numbers will be the topic. When you start breaking up group of digits (numbers) into a function called factors, you will be amazed to find Primes all over the place. For instance, 24 separates or factors into 2/2/2/3, or 28 will be resolved into primes such as: 2/2/7.

The only even number to be a prime is 2. You will find that 5 only appears once as a prime. When you thoroughly understand how to sketch the Sieve of Eratosthenes (circa B.C. 230), you will see that at the beginning the series 2, 3, 5, 7 stops there. After that spot in the Sieve, the only primes to appear become 1, 3, 7, and 9.

2, 3, 5, 7, 11, 13, 17, 19,
23, 29, 31, 37, 41, 43, 47,
53, 59, 61, 67, 71, 73, 79,
83, 89, 97, etc.

To find all the prime numbers from 1 to 100, write the numbers from 1 to 100 in rows of 10 each. Start cancelling all the even numbers except 2. Then every third odd number after 3, every fifth number after 5, every seventh odd number after 7, and so on. This is the Sieve of Eratosthenes.

Another strange feature of primes is that the product of two primes never makes a perfect square amount. While 9 and 4 may make the square of 6, the primes never will.

Lastly, it is purported that if a prime (this does not apply for 2 or 3) is increased or decreased by 1, then the new figure is always divisible by 6. Try it out to convince yourself. Another thing you will notice is that every even integer (not 2 though) is the sum of any two primes: e.g., 5 + 7 = 12; 31+ 53 = 84, etc.

Check in on Chapter 8.1 for more on Primes.

C'MON SPEED... YOU GOTTA GET THAT 'OL CALCULATOR IN YOUR BRAIN WORKING TO BEAT THE MIND BOGGLER
THE MIND BOGGLER

Chapter 7

The true purpose of education is to cherish and unfold the seed of immortality already sown within us; to develop, to their fullest extent, the capacities of every kind with which the God who made us has endowed us.

MRS. JAMESON – Education. Winter Studies and Summer Rambles.

At this point in the Course, let me introduce you to . . .

"The Mind Boggler!"

Yes, I've got a real horror for you guys and gals. From here on in, we will assail your imagination with Instant Exercises.

We expect you to slowly but surely grow day by day into mental giants. This is not a whim on my part. Follow my methods and you will. The real skill of mental calculating becomes an art when you apply yourself totally to the science of arithmetic. You are in school, or university to broaden your mental horizons.

This is a pace-setter. As you are confronted by various mental exercises at different spots in this book, don't think of them as tragic slow-downs, but a real challenge to see if you've really got the stuff of which scientists are made.

Therefore, meet the Mind Boggler #1. As you turn pages, you will be directed to turn to page 35, or maybe 53, even 65. We will ask you to use Table 1, or Table 2, or Table 6, and perform mentally such additions, subtractions, or multiplications found therein. You also will be asked to perform these tasks, and increase or decrease the found values in such Tables by a given amount.

For example: "Turn to Page 56, Table 2, and add 9 to each of the numbers in Rows A, B, C: add 17 to balance of Table."

A few illustrations are shown as follows::

TABLE 2:
Numbers 3 to 99 (approx,)

A	B	C	D	E	F	G	H	I	J	K	L
19	57	63	82	39	61	93	65	38	31	24	17
10	3	96	89	82	75	68	41	54	47	40	33
26	19	12	98	5	84	91	20	77	56	63	49
42	28	35	14	21	93	66	79	58	51	44	37
32	23	9	16	95	11	88	74	67	6	46	53
39	95	36	25	18	11	4	97	83	90	7	69
38	48	41	44	20	27	13	6	99	95	22	85
18	64	57	50	66	43	29	22	78	18	37	49

Exercise No. 8

Mental Addition

Add 17 to each number in Table 1; Increase every number in Table 2, Column H, by 3 to you get to 200.

(+ 17 –> Hint: add 10, and then 7).

Use left-to-right addition, which is done by first adding the tens of one number to the whole number of another. If adding 14 to any number, add the 10 and then the 4. A few examples follow:

17 + 14: think 17, 27, 31.
24 + 14: think 24, 34, 38.
47 + 14: think 47, 57, 61. etc.

Work down the columns – not across the pages. If you want to, write down the answers and compare them to the answers of your partner.

We're going to bounce about a bit from here on in. Exercises will be flashed in different places from time to time. Calculation is an art, a skill and must be sharpened, honed and polished for the difficult times ahead. The world is in a worrisome condition. The best minds will persevere and be successful in business, commerce, trade, construction, high-technology and every myriad and conceivable media.

So, the question is asked: . . . How do I really develop this math skill?

By developing a thing called ***"Number Sense!"*** As I mentioned earlier on these pages, we're all accountants, cashiers, storekeepers, medical men and women, truck drivers, you name us, and that's what we do for a living. But numbers are an intrinsic part of our daily living. We all have number sense. When we were born, we counted our fingers and toes. You don't see adults taking off their shoes and counting their blessings on pay day. But by the same token, many a professional relies on his calculator to do such simple reckonings that a store clerk would consider it "a piece of cake". Einstein could manipulate Relativity, but his wife gave him a quarter and a reminder that "that was for your lunch!" .

To give an example of what is meant by number sense, suppose you were asked to multiply mentally 11625 by 12. If you felt at all competent to try to do so, you would probably (unless you are the exceptional case) proceed like this:

12 times 5 is 60, remember 0 and carry 6; 12 times 2 is 24, plus 6 = 30; put 0 before the other 0 and carry 3, etc. In this way, you would eventually arrive at the correct answer – if you did not get all mixed up in the meantime; but at best you would take a long time, because number sense would have played no part whatever in your awkward method of approaching this very simple little problem.

Suppose now that we introduce a little of this number sense – suppose that instead of dealing with plain figures, you were told to imagine that you had sold twelve machines on each of which you made a commission of $11.62. As soon as money enters into the matter you immediately see the whole picture in a different light.

If you were asked approximately how much your commissions amounted to, you would figure quick as a flash that 11 times 12 is 132, and you would probably answer instantly that you had may be made something over $132. If you were then asked just how much over $132, you would either figure that 62¢ is approximately 5/8 of one dollar (actually 62-1/2 is right on), or else that this amount is equal to half a dollar plus 1/8 of $1.

You would not take long in determining that the excess over $132 comes to $7-1/2, or $7.50, and therefore the total amount received would be $139-1/2 or $139.50.

From this illustration you may correctly infer that the person with ***number sense*** works very largely from left to right instead of from right to left. Left-to-right calculation is of the essence of Number Sense. Countless practical people know this, yet the art of left-to-right calculation is never taught in schools, and is, in fact, rarely mentioned in books of any kind.

Step-by-step instruction and practice in this neglected art of left-to-right calculation constitutes the greater part of the substance of this book. Methods of this kind are applied not only to multiplication but to all the fundamental operations. By means of such methods, for instance, you learn to add two columns of figures at a time, and you even get a little practice with three-column addition. You are also taught comparable methods of subtraction and division.

In addition to the exercises having to do with left-to-right calculations, there are many that are based on an extension of the multiplication table. You are taught by easy stages to use all the numbers up to 50 as direct multipliers – that is to say, you acquire a complete knowledge of the multiplication table up to 55 times 55.

The subject of fractions is treated with special reference to the addition and subtraction of the fractions that are most commonly met with in everyday work. The object here is to enable the student to memorize the answers to the kinds of problems that are ordinarily figured out over and over again.

The final broad subject developed in this book is "Short Cuts." These are of the highest value in developing a general understanding of numbers.

The subject matter of this book is limited to the four fundamental operations, plus the inclusion of fractions and decimals. No attempt is made to consider the various fields of arithmetical application. Skill in calculation pure and simple is the only goal. We do fringe on Algebra, but not totally on it.

The exercises, numerous in number, are for the most part very short. Few should take more than ten minutes to do, and many will take less. As progress is by graded steps, the instruction is in small "doses."

The Course, accordingly, can be used with profit whenever you happen to have a few free minutes. Its pocket size, moreover, makes it all the more suitable for odd-moment study.

Taken as a whole, this book will prove invaluable to anybody engaged in work or study that requires any considerable amount of arithmetical use and handy immediate application to things commercial in the market square. It is especially recommended to heads of departments in industrial and statistical organizations, for general distribution to the members of their staffs.

But enough of the side talk. Motivation is one thing but you've got to have a working Brain to fight the Depression that is rampant in the world today. If you have an open mind, an eager attitude to succeed, and the will to learn, patient parents, coupled with a healthy association with love and friendship, stands to reason you'll survive. There I said it, and undoubtedly I sound like a record of your pals and family. So let's get back to work, or play, whichever comes first.

Motivational Thoughts for the Super Math-e-Magician:

**YOU CAN'T CLIMB THE LADDER TO SUCCESS
IF YOU'RE LAYING DOWN ON THE JOB ALL THE TIME!**

THIS IS A PRIME RIB

THIS IS A PRIME NUMBER
2

Chapter 8

There are three kinds of people:
Those who make things happen;
Those who watch things happen;
and those who bewildered, say "What happened?"

Another Anon.

WHAT'S A PRIME NUMBER?

A positive integer, a whole number, greater than one, that cannot be expressed as a product of two positive integers, neither of which is 1, is known as a prime number. Any positive integer greater than 1 that is not a prime number can be expressed as a product of two or more prime numbers. For example, 4 = 2 x 2; 6 = 3 x 2; 8 = 4 x 2, and so on.

The first few prime numbers 2, 3, 5, 7, 11, etc., are easy to spot. Until 1985 the highest prime number known was 2^{216091} – 1 which written out starts off as:

1701411834604692317316873037158841057 27......

and has over 65,000 digits, The computer took 3 hours to check that this number was indeed prime, working at the rate of 400 million calculations per second. When proved at CRAY supercomputer in Houston, Texas, the BBC at 7:30 a.m. on September 23, 1985 broadcast this as a new record of man's ingenuity. (Any prime number calculated like this automatically results in *the new prime number.*)

Two numbers that were thought to be primes, on the other hand, have lately been shown to have factors. They are:

1757051 (1291 x 1361) and 222221 (619 x 359)

A prime producer:

Let's try 41. Add to itself consecutive multiples of 2. 41 + 2 = 43, next prime up. 41 + 2 + 4 = 47, another prime. 41 + 2 + 4 + 6 = 53, a prime. 41 + 2 + 4 + 6 + 8 = 61, prime. 41 + 2 + 4 + 6 + 8 + 10 = 71, a prime. Try further to see where it breaks down. Where does it become a composite integer?

Eratosthenes, a B.C. type, no not British Columbia, c,183 B.C., devised a square 10 by 10, and wrote all the numbers 1 to 1100 inside it. He then struck out all his prime numbers. 26 prime numbers showed up. He proved himself a mathematician, and became financially secure with the top brass. Try it yourself!

There's something called random numbers. Now what's the word random mean, "Quick-Pick 649!" That's what.

Now random numbers are something else:

Random numbers are not just any number chosen at random, but mathematically, it is a number that cannot be described more solidly than by simply explaining its digits in order. For example: 297,468,349,628,834,932,108,256. (This number could be arrived at by picking numbers out of a hat, or playing with bingo balls and ten minutes to spare to do it. The numbers of a random could be taken to infinity, and in a number sense have no merit whatsoever.

Got a boring day ahead, try this:

Sociable numbers are really odd-ball. A sociable number is one of a chain of numbers whose factors add up to the next number in the chain, with the process repeated until a number is reached whose own factors add up to the first number in that chain. For example: the factors of 12,496 add up to 14,288, whose factors add up to 15,472, whose own factors add up to 14,536, whose own factors add up to 14,264, whose own factors add up to 12,496 (which is where we originally started). Some math type found this chain as far back as 1918, then somebody located another in 1969. Since then computers with nothing to do, but with an operator on salary at the time, found at least 10 sociable links or fewer for all numbers up to 60,000,000. Seven chains were found, each having four links. Such sociable groups of numbers have been nicknamed "crowds".

Back to Prime Numbers!

(Did you read that section about the Sieve of Eratosthenes on page 6.5.) It was supposed to be an introduction for this subject.

Three is a prime number, a number that cannot be evenly divided except by itself and by 1. 1 and 2 are of course prime numbers, the next after 3 is 5, then 7,11,13,17,19 and 23; after that they gradually become increasingly rare. There are a couple of strange things about the first few prime numbers, for example:

$$153 = 1^3 + 5^3 + 3^3$$

And 3 and 5 can also both be expressed as the difference between two squares:

$$3 = 2^2 - 1^2$$
$$5 = 3^2 - 2^2$$

Here's a prime oddity . . . $13^2 = 169$. and $31^2 = 961$. We wonder how many such oddities can you find for yourself?

While we are on the subject of reverse squares, $12^2 = 144$, and $21^2 = 441$. Something strange about numbers!

There are such things as reversible primes, as follows:
The only available digits are 1, 3, 7, and 9. One cannot reverse 5. Hence they produce these prime reversibles: 11, 13 - 31, 17 - 71, 37 - 73, 79 - 97. Can you reason why we didn't use 19 or 93?

Euclid proved that there is no limit to primes. Try multiplying all the primes from 2 through n and add 1. It will give a prime or it will be a composite with a prime factor greater than n. As at the beginning primes are scattered irregularly but with an ever-decreasing frequency amongst the integers. In the first 10 numbers there are 5 integers (50%). 26 or 26% in the first 100, and only 8% in the first million. Look for more primes over that number only if they pay you by the hour. It's not worth it.

The Sieve of Eratosthenes requires a real lengthy explanation, but suffice it to say something about it is needed. The first prime is 2. Between 2 and 100 cross out all multiples of 2. Next comes 3, cross out multiples, etc. Primes stand out few and far between. The largest list ever composed was over 23,000,000. Phew!!

LUCKY
7

Chapter 9

And now into the

BIG TIME SPENDER NUMBER 7!

NUMBER 7 as a Prime has some odd uses in math magic . . . . There is a curious relationship between 7 and the number 142857. Keep your eye on this for a moment.

7 x 2 = 7 x 2 =	14
7 x 2^2 = 7 x 4 =	28
7 x 2^2 = 7 x 8 =	56
7 x 2^4 = 7 x 16 =	112
7 x 2^5 = 7 x 32 =	224
7 x 2^6 = 7 x 64 =	448
7 x 2^7 = 7 x 128 =	896
7 x 2^8 = 7 x 256 =	179 2
7 x 2^9 = 7 x 512 =	3 584
	142857142857142(784)

However far you take the calculation, the sequence 142857 will repeat itself, though the final digits on the right-hand side which we have bracketed will be "wrong" because they would be affected by the next stage in the addition if you took the calculation on further.

This number 142857 has itself some strange properties; multiply it by any number between 1 and 6 and see what takes place:

142857 x 1 = 142857
142857 x 2 = 285714
142857 x 3 = 428571
142857 x 4 = 571428
142857 x 5 = 714285
142857 x 6 = 857142

The same digits recur in each answer, and if the products are each written in the form of a circle, you will see that the order of the digits remains the same. If you then go on to multiply the same number by 7, the answer is 999999. We will come back to some further characteristics of this number later on.

STRANGE ADDITION

3 x 2 =	2 6	2 + 6 = 8 or 2^3
3 x 3 =	3 9 15	3 + 9 + 15 = 27 or 3^3, etc.,
" 4 =	4 12 20 28	
" 5 =	5 15 25 35 45	
" 6 =	6 18 30 42 54 66	
" 7 =	7 21 35 49 63 77 91	
" 8 =	8 24 40 56 72 88 104 120	
" 9 =	9 27 45 63 81 99 117 135 153	

In the table above, the horizontal lines are arithmetical progressions. The difference between each number and the one to its right is twice the figure that stands at the beginning of the row. (Row 7 for example can be worked out by adding 14, first to 7 and to each successive total.) See pp. 81-83.

But how would you find the sum of all the numbers in any row? There is no need to add them – it is the same as the cube of the number which stands at the beginning of that row. For example, the total of the numbers in row 6 is 6 x 6 x 6 =216.

Here's a late addition to this Chapter. Example: 1/17 has a complete decimal period 0.588,235,294,117,647, which, when multiplied by any number from 1 to 16, results in a cyclic permutation of itself. Go one step further, to 17 times, and it results in sixteen 9's. *Strange! Try it!*

You don't have to be a lightning calculator to multiply any number mentally up to and through (?) 7,000.

Example: 142,857 x 11 = 1,571,427 can be shifted to a cyclic permutation of 142,857 by moving the 1st digit to the last space: 1 + 571,427 = 571,428.

Likewise, two digits can be shifted on 8-digit products, and also three digits in 9-digit products.

142,857 x 111 = 15,857,127; 15 + 857,127 = 857,142.
142,857 x 1111 = 158,714,127; 158 + 714,127 = 714,285.

Mental multiplication is very easy with this number. In fact, it was used endlessly in the olden days for stage calculators. If he asked to the audience for a large number, he would write this 142,857 underneath it and start calculating the massive answer multiplying from left to right. It looked fantastic. The man's a genius. "Magnificent! Bravo!!" and so on. What he was doing at a breakneck speed was dividing the number given by the audience through twice by 7

EXERCISE 9
Mental Addition

Add 26 to each of the numbers in Table 2 on page 56.
(Hint: Add 20 to number, then 6, e.g., 47 + 26: 47, 67, 73, etc.)

EXERCISE 10
Left to Right Subtraction – Two digit numbers

Solve the following subtractions by writing your answers from left to right. Note that 9 is greater than 8 in the 1st example. Therefore, the top figure, the minuend 7 falls by 1 to 6. Then 5 from 6 is 1, (mark down 1), 9 from 18 is 9, ans. = 19.

1.	**2.**	**3.**	**4.**	**5.**	**6.**	**7.**	**8.**
78	46	98	94	63	38	57	61
59	17	29	81	48	29	31	48
19							

EXERCISE 11
Left to Right Subtraction – Three digit numbers

Solve the following subtractions by writing your answers from left to right. **Scan for larger numbers in subtrahend first.**

1.	**2.**	**3.**	**4.**	**5.**	**6.**
368	476	928	997	668	388
259	217	329	871	468	299

I CALL THIS
MY PENSA
POSITION

Chapter 10

"H-E-R-E-'S PENSA!"

If you're already members of the internationally acclaimed MENSA, our PENSA stands in its shadow to some extent. But don't let anything deter you from using Pensa as a rung on the ladder to infinite genius. Knowledge comes at you in various ways. Subconscious memory, a fleeting whisper of truth that stays forever in your memories, a trill of a bird that later recalls a picture of your adolescent lives. Sharpen your memory, and dull your sharp tongues. Live is learning. Yearning comes later after your ready for the fast track, and all its compensations.

At our insistence, please read the MENSA books in your libraries. It really lets you know what level of intellect you have attained. If your IQ is not up to par, get cracking, and start studying. Fat or obese in youth means a 90% chance of being obese in adult live. A dull mind as a kid, without drive or eagerness to learn will certainly mean that that is your lot for all times: Dull, boring, and without incentive. Take your pick now, or suffer poverty and crime as your only future. Boy, do I sound pessimistic. But that's the truth! It's in the Book!!!

The author is hoping that these tests are really difficult. If they were not hard, then there's no purpose to review what you already know. So get with it!

This is an introduction to the many MENSA books on the market and readily available through an enquiry at your local librarian. He and/or she will feel a sense of exhilaration by the many students who aspire to mathematical genius. If you wish to tell them that they can get it from this book, feel free to do s

1. What is the next letter in this series:

   O-T-T-F-F-S-S-E-N-?

2. Insert the missing number:

   341 (250) 466
   282 (?) 398

3. 718 (26) 582
   474 (?) 226

4. Insert the missing letter

   A D G
   G K O
   O T ?

5. Insert the missing number.

   3 24 4
   5 120 100
   1 0 ?

6. Insert the missing number.

   4 7 9 11 14 15 19 ?

7. Find the odd man out.

   KEIP
   GEHRNIR
   KRASH
   ROMFERTOC

8. MAIR
   TIGERTIB
   DORHAL
   NOCENI

9. Insert the missing word.

   GRINS (LOIN) ALONE
   SWILL (..........) ATONE

10. STING (SITS) ATOMS
    BLANK (........) CRAMS

11. When I first saw this crummy phone number, I had the feeling that I had seen it before. Can you recall whose number was it?

(314) 159-2654

12. Which of the numbers in the bottom row should be placed under 17 in the top line?

2	3	4	5	6	7	8	10	11	17
7	2	17	6	13	8	3	5	4	?

9 15 20 33 21 25

13. What is X?

3	2	9	6	10
4	8	3	7	3
5	3	2	2	X

14. What number goes in the brackets?

144 (3625) 125
96 (1618) 126
112 (?) 144

15. Which date does not conform with the others?

(a) 1682
(b) 1925
(c) 1543
(d) 1736
(e) 1808

16. What are x, y, and z?

F 6 3 O 15 6 U 21 9
R 18 12 T 20 x y z ?

17. What is the next logical number in this sequence?

3-1/2, 4, 7, 14, 49, ?

18. What is the next number in this sequence, and why?

1, 1, 2, 3, 5, 8, 13, 21, ?

There's an easy way, and a hard way to the answer. Can you find both?

19. Circle odd man out.

208 156 301 289

20. Insert the word missing from the backets.
    87 (high) 98
    53 (. . . .) 16

21. Insert the missing number:
    381 (860) 596
    266 (?) 432

22. Insert the missing number
    8 24 21
    7 35 40
    8 56 ?

23. Insert the missing number
    7 21 18
    21 63 –
    12 24 22

24. Insert the missing number.
    6 14 31 66 ?

25. Insert the missing number.
    4 9 17 35 69 ?

26. Calculate the right answer:
    97.2 ÷ 12.15 x 7.25 =
    a) 58 b) 5.8 c) 60.7

27. Insert missing number
    8 6 3 16
    4 9 6 6
    9 8 – 18

28. Calculate the right answer. If you have to multiply/divide and add/subtrsct, do the multiply/division first:
    12 x 3 ÷ 6 x 0 x 20 ÷ 4 x 5 ÷ 10 =
    a) 150 b) 0 c) 100 d) 6 e) 15

29. Insert missing letter
    D P G S K W N –

30. Insert the missing word
STING (SONS) ROOFS
GROAN (........) ALOUD

31. Figure this one out
$\sqrt{196} + 4^3 - 8^2 \div 4 \div 2 + 2^3 =$
a) 74 b) 80 c) 27.70 d) 70

32. Find the missing number
7 4 15
8 6 20
9 3 –

33. Fractions anyone?
2-1/4 x 4/27 – 4/9 =
a) 3/4 b) 4/27 c) 2-1/12

34. Insert the missing number.
4 10 17 38 71 148 289 ?

35. If $y = (2 - a)^3$, and $a = -2$, then $y =$
a) –64 b) –12 c) 0 d) 12 e) 64

36. $\sqrt{125} + 2\sqrt{20} - 3\sqrt{5} =$
a) $10\sqrt{5}$ b) $6\sqrt{5}$ c) $\sqrt{80}$ d) $\sqrt{30}$ e) 0

37. Insert the missing number.

8	16	(128)	512
14	49	(686)	2744
18	81	(?)	5832

38. Solve this equation:
$2(3x - 5) - 4x = 2 - x$

39. Solve this expression:
2(1/2x + 2) = 2(3)

40. Insert the missing number.
643 (111) 421
269 ( ) 491

(See answers in back of book.)

SO WHAT IF I FAIL ... I'LL JUST LET THE GOVERNMENT SUPPORT ME...
DOES THIS GUY NEED AN ATTITUDE ADJUSTMENT OR WHAT...?
MATH

Chapter 11

ON STAGE EVERYONE . . .

Beware the Goof-Offer, He's No Pal!

You could have the potential to be a mentalist. An honest-to-goodness entertainer – a North American Genius, and what did you do? **NOTHING!** You could have been a perfect student!

The Canadian and American nationals have an abysmal attitude about mathematics – for that matter the same about school. Everyone is out for the Big Con. Get-rich-quick ideas, and that includes mugging, house breaking, etc. It's time to grasp success by the hair and settle down.

There are students from all over the world pouring into our North American continent as immigrants with a desperate yearning to succeed. We look at them and mutter. But they seem to walk all over us when it comes to dedication about their education. Perhaps we have taken it too easy in our domestic way of life. "What the heck, welfare is there! UIC, grants, free-bees – we're never going to have to really work. All we need is a roof over our heads, a case of beer, 649, and the government will take care of us. Just like in Sweden. Guaranteed social relief, from the cradle to the grave. Hah!"

The newly arrived kids look to their parents, and glow in their apparent (pardon the pun) pride of their elders. To let them down is to bring disgrace on the family name. Some students in Japan have done themselves in when they found that they had failed in exams. I trust that I'm making a point here.

We're so far behind on this continent that our governments are wringing their collective hands and bemoaning the spectre of poverty coming like a deadly creeping deadly fog. C'mon, you guys, smarten up while there is still a wind for change. Read the latest White Papers that scream for attention about our standards of education. Damn, and shucks, we have been given a wonderful gift, and we louse it up with drugs, gangs, violence, rape, dishonesty and perversion. I sound like a missionary! – well, I ain't. I think I'm talking a message of doom – there's no one listening. For your one sake, smarten up!

Now look at what you made me do! I just wasted a good page of space to harangue at you. Well, I hope I made my point. I could continue, but I guess if you can't read, and can't compute, I should very well talk to all those others who are normal.

Entertainment! I think that's where I drifted for a moment.

As a westerner once said: "Multi-Minded Mental Marvel!." Now there's a thought. The world is looking for a mathematical messiah. If you could do tricks, mental feats of infinite calculations, and not be designated as an idiot savant, then fortune would be your prize.

Performing your talents, you would have the adulation of the millions, and be bigger and better than the best-paid quarter-back, or designated hitter. Gretzky, Schmetsky, so whose got the strongest brain? Ten years from now, he'll be walking, not skating. Unless he's got a fantastic accountant, what has he got? Think profession! Add showmanship, and your brain will see you through till you're eighty-five (provided you take vitamins!).

Showmanship is a mighty factor in success as a mentalist. Watching TV, you can study the facial expressions, the gestures, the grace and ease of holding their attention. Get yourself a "schitck", a gimmick. But what may you ask would I do? I'm glad you asked.

Your act must be entertaining, agreed? Educational, hey. that's a must! Different? Yup! Novel and different? Yup! But if you're not a showman, forget it. If you have the flair, aptitude, you can get to the top. Hey, look how far John Candy got with humor(?) and stick-to-it-and-I'll-get-to-the -top attitude. Guts!

You must and will develop a patter after a while, and become a polished actor. So you wanted to be a doctor. What better way to cure than with a laugh and a giggle. Disney's *Pluto* is credited with a miracle cure. The person watching his antics burst out in laughter, and this from a person mute for thirty years. Now he's called *St. Pluto. the Disney star*.

Your presentation is based upon your background. First, you've got to be presentable, but better than that, you've got to be a math-e-magician!

"And just where do I get my material?" Use your brain! Joe Miller (a comic from the old vaudeville days) was noted for his jokes, and every one he stole from somebody's patter from another time. *Uncle Milty* (Milton Berle) stole so many so often, the real originators had to steal them back. "If it was good enough for Milty, hey, I must use that one.*"There's nothing new under the sun* " . . . an adage well-worn out!

Get some gags. Time is of the essence. Plot out a half-hour or even an hour show. Take count of the gags, the seconds can add up to minutes. You don't have to be working all the time.

When you feel comfortable with the pace you have developed, then post your ads, sell your tickets, get an agent, and start earning.

Your brain is like sponge. Cram the mental formulae into it. Be a whiz kid! Startle them with your wit; make them cringe with the amazing recall you've developed. Fortify your act with splendid flashes of memory. Let figures flow like a fountain from your lips. In other words, you're an entertainer of great magnitude. A veritable genius that people talk about to their friends. "Impossible?" What's impossible! ***Unless*** you try!

Now for the presentation you search to acquire. Can you rattle off cubes to great lengths; square numbers in a frenzy of answers? Listen to your audience flinging numbers at you – add them in your head and toss them back in seconds. Now that's *real* showmanship!

"But where do I get my material?" ***The library!***

Every stage calculator, novice or expert researched his act. Have time to bother the Reference Desk for titles. The librarians get paid to be detectives of missing book-lore. And they all went to university and colleges. Unless you open the doors of your mind, they can't help you.

Contained in this book is a vast amount of very scientific mathematical data. Twist the real figures to meet the requirements of your trade. Help some poor devil who can't do his math properly. Just teaching him makes you his mentor. And who knows you'll someday need him/her as a friend.

The PATTER of Little Feats!

While you're making up your collective mind, let's try a few ice breakers. Start off small and grow with your confidence.

- **How to make money!** (You're on stage facing an audience.)

"Does anyone here want to know how to make extra money? Well, I've discovered an easy way. But it takes capital, not much, but some. I put $50 bucks in the bank the other day, and no sooner had I put it in, I had to draw out $20. That left me $30. Next day, I drew out half of that $30. That left me $15. I'm going broke fast. Rather than taking out $15 and leave zero, I took out $9, and I still had $6 to my name. But what do you get for $6 nowadays, so next day I took it out. (All the time I'm facing the audience, writing the figures in two columns, so they get the hang of my spending:

Draw Out	Leaves
$20	$30
15	15
9	6
6	0
$50	$51

When I add up both columns, so help me, I made me a buck! Tried that 20 times the next week, and I"m still broke. **How come?**

Now that's only an ice breaker! You got a laugh and a giggle. Then you ask your audience to sit forward on their seats and hold their collective breath. After 10 seconds, say: ""OK, folks, as you were. I was told that it would be *impossible* to have such a large and friendly audience as you sitting forward on the edges of their seats holding their breath, waiting for my very next words. I do thank you for your confidence in me!"

"For my next offering, may I have a volunteer from the audience." Everyone loves to see a volunteer take a ribbing from the performer. It's in the book. They expect it, so do it.

"Before I get into larger and larger numbers – I had a terrible time in school. I remember I left school at a very early age. Not because I wanted to, school was terrific! That first grade was wonderful, but second grade was a catastrophe. Those teachers made me so nervous I cut myself shaving!"

"Would you folks call out some big numbers, none of those little ones like zeros and ones, and keep them coming." With these numbers, you start to fill a heavy workload. But don't sweat. It's all for a worthy cause. ('Cause you need the money!) And problems? You know Short Cuts 1- 100 will get you out of most of them. Hidden away in Short Cuts is the basis of your act.

Take TTFM, page 23.4 – a Short Cut by Jakow Tractenberg for instance: a person calls a large number, which you copy: 362,282 times 968. Quick as a flash, you start writing down the answer (in this case from right to left). Sharply, with chalk, you write 6, 7, 9, 8, 8, 6, 0, 5, 3. That's it! **The answer is 350,688,976.** Take your bow, and continue on. They rise up in their seats, applauding for minutes. Wow!

The routines are all in these chapters. The different approaches to mental magic: read and memorize all you can in your spare time. Read and digest this SUPER MATH-E-MAGICS.

GOOD LUCK! I really mean it! I've worked out 10 numbers by 10, and it felt great to know I can still do it. You can do it faster by using the Units-Tens Method at the back of the book in Chapter 23.3.

I know you are a bit tired – so take a well-deserved Break!

Here's some odd numbers that bear watching.

11 x 11 = 121
111 x 111 = 12321
1111 x 1111 = 1234321
11111 x 11111 = 123454321
111111 x 111111 = 12345654321
1111111 x 1111111 = 1234567654321
11111111 x 11111111 = 123456787654321
111111111 x 111111111 = 12345678987654321

Here's something very odd!

$$121 = \frac{22 \times 22}{1 + 2 + 1}$$

$$12321 = \frac{333 \times 333}{1 + 2 + 3 + 2 + 1}$$

$$1234321 = \frac{4444 \times 4444}{1 + 2 + 3 + 4 + 3 + 2 + 1}$$

$$123454321 = \frac{55555 \times 55555}{1 + 2 + 3 + 4 + 5 + 4 + 3 + 2 + 1}, \text{ etc.}$$

Note: the denominator of the fraction has the same digits as whole number with + signs in between. The digits in numerator are the centre number of whole number and there are as many digits in numerator as middle digit of the whole number indicates.

Another number twister is this one: **The old mystic 76923!**

76923 x 1 = 076923
76923 x 10 = 769230
76923 x 9 = 692307
76923 x 12 = 923076
76923 x 3 = 230769
76923 x 4 = 307692

The number 76923, when multiplied by 1, 10, 9, 12, 3, and 4 gives the same sequence of digits read up, down and across. All rows add up to 27, and diagonally, left to right are the same number, namely 3.

Now when the same number 76923, is multiplied by 2, 7, 5, 11, 6, and 8 gives off the same sequence of numbers, 153846, read up and down and across. Even the diagonal, when read left up to right corner are all the same, 6.

Magic Calendar Phenomenon

You can thank the stage calculators for this one. It showed up in the '40s.

Have your guest choose any month from your pocket calendar. Ask that he draw a square box around any four dates.

1	2	3	4	5	6	7
8	9	10	11	12	13	14
15	16	17	18	19	20	21
22	23	24	25	26	27	28
29	30	31				

"Add the four numbers in the box, and tell me the total." Wait while he tallies up the answer. Quick ss a flash, you tell the spectators the four dates he boxed. How does it work?

As long as he boxes four dates in a square, the sum he gives is instantly divided by four and then you further reduce this new answer by four. For example: Suppose he has boxed

12 13
19 20

the total is 32 (19 + 13) or (12 + 20) crisscross addition, or a total of 64. When divided by 4 = 16, and further reduced by another 4 = 12. 12 + 1 = 13; 12 + 7 = 19 + 1 = 20. (applause?)

Further, a vertical 3-figure box can be done. Same rules but divide by 3 and subtract 3. Dates chosen may be 15, 22, 29. Total = 66 ÷ 3 = 22. To find dates, subtract 7 from 22 = 15; add 7 to 22 = 29. Q. Will it work if box is drawn horizontally on the same line? Yes. Plus 1 to right, minus 1 to left.

JUST CALL ME
MR. POWER
?
142,857

Chapter 12

And now meet Mr. POWER himself . . .

142,857 !

Keep your eye on his manageable yet most mystical powerful half-brother, 142,857,143. Here's how he was born. (P.S.: He's ninth generation!)

When you factor 111111, by a division of 7, you get 15873, so

111111 = 7 x 15873
222222 = 7 x 31746
333333 = 7 x 47619
444444 = 7 x 63492
555555 = 7 x 79635
666666 = 7 x 95328
777777 = 7 x 111111
888888 = 7 x 126984
999999 = 7 x ***142857***
. . . the BIG fellow!

Keep Your Eye on This Number

142857 x 1 = **142857** x 7 = **0999999** ÷ **9**
142857 x 3 = **428571** x 7 = **2999997** ÷ **9**
142857 x 2 = **285714** x 7 = **1999998** ÷ **9**
142857 x 6 = **857142** x 7 = **5999994** ÷ **9**
142857 x 4 = **571428** x 7 = **3999996** ÷ **9**
142857 x 5 = **714285** x 7 = **4999995** ÷ **9**

When all numbers containing the digits 142857 are multiplied by 7, we get 5 columns of 99999, plus the first and last numbers which add to 9. And note that 142857, is a very odd-ball number, when multiplied by 1, 3, 2, 6, 4, 5, gives the same sequence of digits when read up, down and diagonally. Also every row adds up to 27, just the same as magic number 76923. Interested? Read on.

If you use 111111 and factor it, you will have 111111 = 3 x 37037. So! I'm glad you asked.

111 111 = 3 x 37037
222222 = 6 x 37037
333333 = 9 x 37037
444444 = 12 x 37037
555555 = 15 x 37037
666666 = 18 x 37037

Let's try some more weird and strange arrangements of the science of Arithmetic. This will intrigue you, I hope.

• *1089 – a marvelous number!*

A		*B*
1089 x 1 = 1089	Reversed	9801
" x 2 = 2178		8712
" x 3 = 3267		7623
" x 4 = 4356		6534
" x 5 = 5445		5445
" x 6 = 6534		4356
" x 7 = 7623		3267
" x 8 = 8712		2178
" x 9 = 9801		1089

Notice how the eye travels down one side and up the other. The rhythm of the numbers increasing one by one, first the outside walls of the columns, then the reversing up the middle columns. Also look at the double mating of 1st and 2nd columns vertically, and then going up the opposite direction climbing up the 3rd and 4th columns. Its pattern shows the symmetry of numbers and the overall ordered and yet mystic results when you break numbers in personal research. Try your hand at new and provocative experimentation. Who knows, maybe you're the next Euler, or Waring. Don't hide your brain in someone else's shadow.

Did you ever consider 19 and his mate 9109?

19 x 1 = 19 and 1 + 9 = 10 and 1 + 0 = 1
19 x 2 = 38 and 3 + 8 = 11 and 1 + 1 = 2
19 x 3 = 57 and 5 + 7 = 12 and 1 + 2 = 3
19 x 4 = 76 and 7 + 6 = 13 and 1 + 3 = 4
19 x 5 = 95 and 9 + 5 = 14 and 1 + 4 = 5
19 x 6 = 114 and 11 + 4 = 15 and 1 + 5 = 6
19 x 7 = 133 and 13 + 3 = 16 and 1 + 6 = 7
19 x 8 = 152 and 15 + 2 = 17 and 1 + 7 = 8
19 x 9 = 171 and 17 + 1 = 18 and 1 + 8 = 9
19 x 10 = 190 and 19 + 0 = 19 and 1 + 9 =10

Start messing around with numbers and this happens!

9109 x 1 = 0 9 1 0 9 add digits = 19
9109 x 2 = 1 8 2 1 8 add digits = 20
9109 x 3 = 2 7 3 2 7 add digits = 21
9109 x 4 = 3 6 4 3 6 add digits = 22
9109 x 5 = 4 5 5 4 5 add digits = 23
9109 x 6 = 5 4 6 5 4 add digits = 24
9109 x 7 = 6 3 7 6 3 add digits = 25
9109 x 8 = 7 2 8 7 2 add digits = 26
9109 x 9 = 8 1 9 8 1 add digits = 27

As you can see, these columns run from 1 to 9 and reverse 9 to 1. And the far right column shows a progression of one. Got a flower garden made of numbers. These figures are well read.

Rigid and Eye-Catching!

1 x 8 +1 = 9
12 x 8 + 2 = 98
123 x 8 + 3 = 987
1234 x 8 + 4 = 9876
12345 x 8 + 5 = 98765
123456 x 8 + 6 = 987654
1234567 x 8 + 7 = 9876543
12345678 x 8 + 8 = 98765432
123456789 x 8 + 9 = 987654321

Let's do it again with 9's.

0 x 9 + 1 = 1
1 x 9 + 2 = 11
12 x 9 + 3 = 111
123 x 9 + 4 = 1111
1234 x 9 + 5 = 11111
12345 x 9 + 6 = 111111
123456 x 9 + 7 = 1111111
1234567 x 9 + 8 = 11111111
12345678 x 9 + 9 = 111111111
123456789 x 9 + 10 = 1111111111

What happened to 8 lately?

9 x 9 + 7 = 88
9 x 98 + 6 = 888
9 x 987 + 5 = 8888
9 x 9876 + 4 = 88888
9 x 98765 + 3 = 888888
9 x 987654 + 2 = 8888888
9 x 9876543 + 1 = 88888888
9 x 98765432 + 0 = 888888888
9 x 987654321 – 1 = 8888888888

enuf already?

Simulated Mental Calculator

The majority of the arithmetical operations performed by lightning calculators can be simulated; that is, replaced by others which resemble them only in appearance and are different in method.

DIVISION

What else can you say about division,
except that it's the reverse of multiplication.

The rule is: A factor is either one, two or more numbers which are multiplied together form a product. If 6 x 7 = 42, both 6 and 7 are factors of 42. Therefore, every factor of a product is a divisor of the product. Then, these factors of any given number are all numbers which can be divided into that number with a remainder of zero (0). Take 20, as an example. It breaks down in these factors: 20, 10, 5, 4, 2, 1. Again, 1 and 20 divide as is universally understood, then we won't discuss that alliance.

Let's look at prime numbers.1, 2, 3, 5, 7, 9, 11, 13, 17, 19, 23, etc. If 36 is examined, it may be factored: 1, 2, 3, 4, 6, 9, 18. Of these factors, only 2, 3, 9 are prime factors. Hence 36 in prime factor terms = 2 x 2 x 9 or 2 x 2 x 3 x 3 or various combinations. All prime numbers, except 2 and 5, must have 1, 3, 7, 9 as their units digit. Also it is noted, any integer that has 2 as a factor is an even number.

Division is the inverse of multiplication

In multiplication: a x b = c

In division: c ÷ b = a, or c ÷ a = b. That's plain enough! For example: 24 ÷ 8 = 3, then 8 x 3 = 24 – 3 and 8 are factors or 24. Thus, we can get the factors of a number by dividing successfully by its exact divisors, which usually means by trial and error. On the other hand, Short Cuts in this book does remedy some of your wasted time looking for proper factors. Read Page 25 and put these rules to memory. Check Short Cuts 4, 8, 10, 20, 22, 27, 35 - 37. Scan Short Cuts, it's worth it.

Find the Greatest Common Divider by expressing the given numbers in terms of their prime numbers. Eg.: Find G.C.D. of 108 –> 2 x 2 x 3 x 3 x 3 = 108. Both 2, 3 are prime.

KEEP YOUR EYE ON THE MAGIC NUMBER!

Chapter 13

Magic Numbers abound in the Land of Math – Are you ready for this trip?

Back in Chapter 5, did you notice how much Supplementary and Complementary Multiplications perked you up when you finally caught on to the zigs and zags of mental calculations?

Numbers that were close to 100, 1,000, or even higher and close to each other were manipulated by subtracting them from 100, or even 50, and combinations of 100 and 50 were introduced for the first time in the mental mode. Well, here's a further step into new math magic hunting!

Chapter 16 deals with squares and square roots. But Complementary and Supplementary methods intermingle with such mental logic. For instance, 94^2! We see it as 94 x 94 = **8836**. Boomerang-method, page 5.5!

Complementary-wise: 100 – 94 = 6
100 – 94 = 6

Same logic as before 94 minus 6 = 88 (first side of answer), 6 x 6 = 36. Put in the now old-fashioned sequence you arrive at the answer: **8836**. QED.

This represent another way of squaring, and finer still, not as many headaches! **As we mentioned before, learn all squares from 1 to 50!**

Similarly, rising above 100, or above 50, and the like steps of 25 and 75, we can add above 100 or 50, or subtract as before below 100, or 50. etc.

Above 100, let's square 114, or 114^2, noting the difference of 14 is added to 114 = 128(00), (the left hand side of answer), 14 x 14 or 14^2 = 196 (this is the easy part of this calculation (Boomerang Stage 1, remember?). Now we have the right side 196. Shuffle 12800 + 196, and the 1 of 196 increases 128 up to 129. The complete answer is 12996. Glad you agree!!

Remember, when you are working with larger numbers, in around 1,000 or even 1,500, be wise to estimate the size of the answer in total digits.

Example: Above 1000: $1{,}017^2$

As before: Above 1000, let's square 1,017, noting the difference of 17 is added to 1017 = 1034(000), (the left hand side of answer), 17 x 17 or 17^2 = 289 (this is the easy part of this calculation, Boomerang Stage 1, remember?). Now we have the right side 289, Shuffle 1034000 + 289, and the complete answer is 1034289!!

Further, let's try lower than 1,000: 983^2
Difference this time is a negative (–) minus 17, minus from 983. That leaves the left hand thousands as 966(000). The difference now has to squared: 17 x 17 = (Boomer Stage 1 – 17 + 7 = 24(0) + (7 x 7 = 49) = 289. *Not much left to do now, but shove them together for the right answer:* ***966,289****. Got the hang of it yet? I thought you would! Fantastic!*

When you get number around the 80's or really any number near a zero, try Up Some and Down Some.

For instance: 89^2 = (89 + 1) (89 – 1) = 90 x 88 or better yet 88 x 90 = 7920. Remember? Square the Up Some to The Down Some? Right: 1 x 1 = 1. **The answer is 7920 + 1 = 7921.** Right again! Hey we're on a roll!

As an experimenter in high-speed or rapid calculation, I keep going back to the Boomerang Method. Especially when any combination falls under the 100 level. In fact it's downright fun to whip off the answers in seconds.

97 x 31, 36 x 21, 54 x 41, etc.

You can almost see the answer as they call out the questions. For instance: 97 x 31. 97 + 1 = (thinking in a left to right mode) 98 x 3 of (**3**1) = 294(0). All you have to do now is multiply units 7 x 1= 7. 2940 + 7 = 2947. Still partial. Remember? Difference between 9 and 3 is 6 – (this value of 6 is a tens digit), 1947 + 60 = 3007. Practice these for a few minutes and you can do them in a flash!

Looking at 36 x 21. You take it! (36 + 1 = 37) x 2 = 74(0) + 6 x 1 = 746; difference 3 – 2 = 1(0) = 756. Getting shorter, isn't it?

Faster, still faster:
54 x 41 = 54 + 1 = 55 x 4 = 220(0) + (4 x 1) = 4 = 2204; diff. = 1 x 1 = 1(0) = 2214. And so on.

Yet another version which I learned from an academic-type navigation officer during the war, in Northern Ireland, went as follows:

54 x 41 = 54 x 4 = 216(0). Add top line 54; 216(0) + 54 = 2214.

61 x 41 = 61 x 4 = 244(0). Add top line 61; 244(0) + 61 = 2501.

71 x 21 = 71 x 2 = 142(0). Add top line 71; 142(0) + 71 = 1491.

This is shorter, but only good for numbers ending in 1. The Boomerang won't come back if you use this technique for other multiplications. ***When in doubt, stick with the Boomerang mode.*** *Be consistent in thinking.*

Let's Talk FRACTIONS!

To understand Fractions, let's just look at one – **1/2**! Sheesch! "So? I've seen that before!" Have you seen it as a percentage? Or as a decimal? Take a decco at the conversion table below.

Conversion Table

Fraction	***Percentage***	***Decimal***
1/2	50	.5
1/3	33.33	.3333
1/4	25	.25
1/5	20	.20
1/6	16.67	.1667
1/7	14.29	.1429
1/8	12.5	.125
1/9	11.11	.1111
1/10	10	. 1
1/11	9.09	.0909
1/12	8.33	.0833
1/13	7.69	.0769
1/14	7.14	.0714
1/15	6.67	.0667

If we discuss number as being whole numbers, we mean: 1, 4, 7, 19, etc. But if talk about Fractions, we mean portions of whole numbers. Then one-half or a third of something, even or odd numbers, we show that as 1/2, or 13-1/3 of something. Whether it be money, apples, odds in a game – fractions are talked about as part of our daily language. "Hi, Bob, got a half a dollar on you?" "What period is it? How are the Leafs doing?"

It's important to reduce to its lowest term in order to be a valued figure. You wouldn't ask for 6/8ths of a kilo of ham. You would be chucked out the meat market! You'd ask for 3/4 of a kilo. I guess, come to think of it, they still wouldn't understand. I usually just ask for $3.00's worth!

A common fraction is a number of a math form a/b. The top number (a) is the *numerator*, and can be any number (1, 2, 5, 6, 9, 16, 78, 212, etc.).

The lower number is the denominator; it, too, can be any number, but never a zero (0), (1, 2, 4, 7, 19. 312, etc.) With such high numbers you might have to factor a smaller answer.

An example of fractions are as follows: 3/8, 9/16, 9/8, 144/288. The denominator tells you how many equal pieces it had before becoming a fraction of its former self.

For instance, 3/8 means the whole number is divided into 8 equal portions and we are interested in only 3 of them at this place in time.

Fractions are like people. Some are proper, and other are improper.

Proper Fractions: numerator is less than denominator: 5/8, 2/3.
Improper Fractions: Numerator greater than denominator: 7/5.
Unit Fractions: Numerator and denominator equal: 4/4, 76/76.

For instance, 13/15, it's the same as saying 13 ÷ 15, 5/5 is 5 ÷ 5, 0/6 is 0 ÷ 6, 48/6 is 48 ÷ 6, etc. In other words, a fraction is the same as a division. And we'll discuss that now.

Example: The division of an improper fraction (11/8), comes up as 1-3/8. This new form is called a mixed number. When using this answer, we refer to it as one and three-eighths, or 1 + 3/8. If there is further work to be done on the fraction, reduce it to its lowest terms by factoring it. Eg.: 12/8 = 1-4/8 = 1-1/2.

To reduce a fraction to its lowest terms, find a number (no, not 1) dividing evenly into both numerator and denominator. This includes prime numbers, too. Keep reducing until "no further" flag goes up.

Example: Reduce 30/60 to lowest terms.
1) 2 divides 30 and 60 evenly and with no remainder.
2) 30 ÷ 2 = 15; 60 ÷ 2 = 30;
3) 5 divides 30 and 60 evenly;
4) 15 ÷ 5 = 3; 30 ÷ 5 = 6, no remainder;
5) 3 divides 3 and 6, evenly;
6) 3 ÷ 3 = 1; 6 ÷ 3 - 2.
Therefore, 30/60 = 1/2.

Strip off zeros if they appear in both numerator and denominator. If you have to build a fraction either top (Numerator) or bottom (denominator), such as make 7/8 a fraction with a denominator of 32, Think this way:
the 8 of 7/8 is divided into the 32 = 4.
Then the 7 must be multiplied by the same amount.
7 x 4 = 28. New fraction is 28/32

Multiplication of Common Fractions

No LCD (least common denominator) is needed.
1) Multiply all the numerators together, making the numerator product.
2) Similarly, multiply the denominator to obtain a new product.

Example: $\frac{5}{9} \times \frac{4}{5} = ?$

$$\frac{5}{9} \times \frac{4}{5} = \frac{5 \times 4}{9 \times 5} = \frac{20}{45} = \frac{4}{9}$$

$\frac{4}{9}$ is $\frac{4}{5}$ of $\frac{5}{9}$

Division of Common Fractions

The reverse of Multiplication is Division. To divide a fraction by another, invert the divisor. 2/7 ÷ 5/8. Flip the 5/8 over and it now becomes 8/5.

Example: $\frac{2}{7} \times \frac{8}{5} = \frac{2 \times 8}{7 \times 5} = \frac{16}{35}$

You've got a chocolate bar. Your sister wants a piece. So you give her a third (1/3). You're about to take a big crunch and in pops your friend. "How's about a bite?" So you give him a half (1/2). So how much is left for you? 1/2 of 2/3! A big 1/3, yipes!

In reality you lost 1/3 to sister, you had 2/3 of it left, and then cut your 2/3's in half (1/3 + 1/3), and friend got 1/3. Chocolate's fattening anyway! *They did you a favour.*

Multiplication and division is simplified by cancelling or dividing the numerator (50) and denominator (75) by the same values of related numbers, in this case a 25 changes 50/75 into 2/3 instantly. 6/9 becomes 2/3, etc. Less cumbersome in the end.

FRACTION SHORT CUTS

Leaving division for a moment, if you must multiply fractions, you can use addition as a Short Cut.

Example: $\frac{1}{7} \times \frac{1}{6} = \frac{13}{42}$

1) Add denominators for numerator: 7 + 6 = 13.
2) Multiply for denominator: 7 x 6 = 42
3) Answer is **13/42.** That's all!

Another sample: but different: $\frac{3}{5} \times \frac{1}{4} = \frac{17}{20}$

1) Cross multiply for numerator
   3 x 4 = 12; 5 x 1 = 5; and add 12 + 5 = 17.
2) Multiply for denominator – 5 x 4 = 20.
3) You're finished. Answer is **17/20**. That's all. And easy, quick!

So far, we've multiplied, divided, added, but we have not touched subtraction. So let's turn the page and get with it. Please remember, if you're already at school, this is all past experiences. Maybe this geared for the older persons, huh?

SUBTRACTING FRACTIONS

As before in addition, find a common denominator. In order to solve such subtraction, the lowest common denominator must be found. In the case of our sample below, we solve the LCD by multiplying 4 x 3 = 12.

$$\frac{3}{4} - \frac{1}{3} = \frac{9-4}{12} = \frac{5}{12}$$

$$\frac{3}{4} + \frac{1}{3} + \frac{4}{5} - \frac{2}{3} = \frac{?}{?}$$

Find the LCD for this one (?): 3 x 4 x 5 = 60, 120, 240? Ans. 60.

$$\frac{3}{4} + \frac{1}{3} + \frac{4}{5} - \frac{2}{3} = \frac{?}{?}$$

Get the brain working. Start with the 3/4 and LCD 60. 60 ÷ 4 = 15, or 4 goes into 60 evenly 15 times. Multiply 15 by the 3 of 3/4. 3 into 60 = 20 x 1=20, etc to the right. Now your calculation is ready for adding and subtracting.

$$\frac{15}{60} + \frac{20}{60} + \frac{48}{60} - \frac{40}{60} = \frac{83-40}{60} = \frac{43}{60}$$ Answer.

Another SHORT CUT – Multiplying by a number nearly whole

Once in a while a multiplier need but a single slight unit to become a whole number. Say, 6-3/4, 9-7/8, etc. Only missing 1/3, 1/8, 1/6, and so forth, to become a whole.Let's raise the multiplier to the next higher number. Multiply the multiplicand by this new number. Now subtract from the product that fractional part you used in the first place. Let's multiply 48 x 4-5/6: we multiply 48 by 5 = 240, and then we subtract 1/6 of 48 = 8, and our final answer is 232. Try a few of your own. 1. 48 x 5-3/4, 2, 342 x 9-5/6, 3. 522 x 4-8/9, etc.

Let's have an Exercise 10-minute break here.

TABLE 4: Add each column, starting from the left-hand side of the number. Square the respective answer of each column, using the Short Cut No. 65 (where indicated raise or lower these numbers by whatever unit values suggested).

TABLE 4:

A	B	C	D	E	F	G	H
52	83	44	35	69	77	88	99
12	13	16	18	45	104	23	12
16	67	62	79	89	76	54	32
55	31	30	58	62	79	97	22
12	19	26	52	23	53	88	69
67	49	31	95	49	98	211	26
34	45	72	93	14	21	66	84
39	11	24	21	35	51	59	58

Scratch your work here in case you have no workpad!

Card Trick . . . Conclusion!

Back on page 2.9 I gave an exercise in casting out 10's. There was an interesting aftermath (no pun intended!) to this labourious task. If you've developed speed and accuracy in coming up with the ultimate answer of 4 (FOUR), then have I got a trick for you.

And this is how it goes: In presenting this card trick, your audience will stand amazed as you turn a card over, and say: "Queen of Clubs!" "Wait, let's see you do that again!"

Shuffle the cards, expose the lot face upwards, and ask a spectator to verify the pack as clean and new. S/he will then pass the collected pack to you, after having cut the cards and removing a single card, keeping the cards and the selected cards face down. You can cut further if you so desire.

At this point, you start adding the cards face upward, exposing each at the same pace. All the time you're turning these you maintain a silent 10-count of values as described on page 2.9: 7, 9 (16, think 6), 6, 5 (11, think 1), K (3, think 4), 4 (think 8), Q (2, think 10 –> think zero), etc., always adding without ever passing the 10's threshold. Your count should be silent: 7, 6, 2, 7, 0, 1, 5, 7, etc. (Remember Jack = 1, Queen = 2, King = 3, as does Ace, 2, 3 have the same value.

Towards the end of your count, you start running out of cards. Naturally! Now comes the dreaded task. As you cast out 10's, the finale gets supposedly tougher. You squint, take an audible deep breath, "h-m-m-m!" several times. After all, remembering 52 different cards, both colours, mentally placing each card in a slot order and in series is a mighty horrible mental workout!

If the last two or three cards keep the 10 value still not deducted, and on the last cards, it does exceed 10, take what last card count you have left and subtract it from 14. Say the count was 12, from 14 that leaves 2. The hidden card is 2. Remember that 2 and the Queen have the same count value.

Scan the cards quickly for four 2's or Queens missing. Three Queens and four 2's. All Queen's suits are there but the clubs. Triumphantly, with a huge smile, you declare "The Queen of Clubs!" and turn the card over, revealing the Queen of Clubs.

"Terrific! Do that one again! You're a genius, a real mentalist!" "How did you ever get to have such a fantastic memory!!"

Leonardo Fibonacci's Trick

Mathematician, scholar, scientist, an all-round good fellow. Just one problem, though. He was born in and around 1235 A.D. Mind you, he worked himself into the history books because he was dedicated in seeing, thinking about what he saw, and digging into the reasons why such a thing did what it did. In other words, an enquiring mind and an experimenter.

Fibonacci Series are familiar to math types, and here's a novel way to use Ol' Fibs expertise:

Each number in the series is the sum of the two numbers before it. Supposing that you started with two single digits, 6 and 8, you must add these two to make a sum of 14. Then add 8 and 14 to get 22, and add 14 to 22 to get 36, and so on.

```
   6
   8
  14
  22
  36
  58
  94 ← seventh number down
 152
 246
 398 ← tenth level
────
1034
```

The total of the 10 numbers is 1,034. As the trick is taking place, keep your eye on the 7th level. As soon as your audience has computed the mounting sum for the 7th level and forge on to the 10th and final stage, you multiply the 7th level (94) by 11= 1034, and that's the final total for the column. After seeing the 7th number, step back. Insist that the total not be seen by yourself. Dramatically read the mind of the spectator: "1034!"

Another whiz kid! ***A real rapid-calculation by a top-notch stage calculator!***

What's CALCULUS All About?

Some time in the near future, you will face the challenges of the world, or even now at whatever age you have succeeded in getting to this date. Someone somewhere is going to ask you: "Hey! Whatcha' know about CALCULUS?" No, he wasn't a Roman Emperor. No, it's not a mineral. It's a name given to deal with problems of matters as the changing of speeds, varying pressure changes in the supports of bridges, speed of light, circuits. No! Not the racing circuit, Electrical circuits!

In general, Calculus is the studying of various quantities which are always in the state of flux or continually varying.

Calculus has different forms: INTEGRAL Calculus – it deals with a method of adding together the effects of continuously varying quantities.

DIFFERENTIAL Calculus uses a similar mode dealing with rates of change. If you're fooling around with speed (motion, that is), this is your bag, man.

Each of these branches of Calculus probes into problems of small quantities which during that process are made smaller and smaller, and that introduces us to little brother Calculus – INFINITESIMAL Calculus.

Differential equations represent complex rates of change and integrals are the empirical solutions. When you don't know the right process and are boxed for an answer, these integrations are made graphically or perhaps by a computer or machine.

You can blame Archimedes back in the 3rd. century B.C. He stumbled upon a way of finding the areas of curved figures and for drawing tangents to these curves. So he said, "forget it!", and it wasn't until the 17th century when Descartes proved that geometrical curves could be drawn, described and also analyzed by means of algebra. He presented many formulae, and gained notoriety for the discovery. Then along comes Fermat, then later on Newton and Leibniz. Then Calculus really took off. So you see there's still room for improvement in the world of Math. Perhaps your name will be next in history!

GO AHEAD... PICK A CARD FROM MY IMAGINARY DECK AND I'LL TELL YOU WHAT IT IS...

Chapter 14

Trick or Treat Time!

"SUPER MATH-E-MAGICS"

Now comes a bit of Stage work of a somewhat different kind which is also rather original.

The performer turns to a spectator and says "Without knowing anything about you I am going to give you the number of your destiny, that is, the number which is dominant in your life. It is 3,988. When were you born?" The spectator may say, "1940." "And your wife? (Or girl friend)" "1945." "Now, if you write down those two dates and your respective ages at your last birthdays – that is, 54 and 49 – and add them all together, you will find 3,988. This number is that which dominates your whole existence since it is formed with dates which are important to you."

In reality this number would have been the same for any person. It is the double of the current year, here 1994. If a third person also asks for his destiny number, he can be given the triple of the current year, in which case it will be necessary to add the date of birth and the age of one of his children.

Multiple Practices

Interesting to amaze you friends!

1. Ask him/her to write down the following number: twelve million, three hundred and forty-five thousand, six hundred and seventy-nine. Beware: Use the long version: twelve million, etc., not 12,345,679 (12,345,679). (Note that the number eight is omitted.)

2. Now ask your friend which number of all these he likes the least, and when he gives you his answer, tell him to place an "x" above the number he has selected.

3. At this point, instruct him to multiply the original 12,345,679 by a number which you suggest.

4. Once he multiplies as directed, he will find that every figure in his total corresponds to the number above which he placed the "x".

Example:

```
         x
  12,345,679
          45
 -----------
  61,728, 395
 493, 827, 16
 ------------
 555, 555, 555
```

Explanation:

It really doesn't matter what number your friend selects. Merely multiply that number by 9. Thus, in the case shown above, you multiply 5 x 9 and get 45. Once you have this total, multiply 12,345,679 by it.

The number 12,345,679 has some interesting features, for example:

12,345,679 x 3 = <u>037,037,037</u>	
12,345,679 x 30 = 370,370,370	<u>Totals 30</u>
12,345,679 x 57 = 703,703,703	
12,345,679 x 6 = <u>074,074,074</u>	
12,345,679 x 33 = 407,407,407	<u>Totals 33</u>
12,345,679 x 60 = 740,740,740	
12,345,679 x 12 = <u>148,148,148</u>	
12,345,679 x 39 = 481,481,481	<u>Totals 39</u>
12,345,679 x 66 = 814,814,814	

12,345,679 x 15 = 185,185,185
12,345,679 x 42 = 518,518,518 Totals 42
12,345,679 x 69 = 851,851,851

12,345,679 x 21 = 259,259,259
12,345,679 x 48 = 592,592,592 Totals 48
12,345,679 x 75 = 925,925,925

12,345,679 x 24 = 296,296,296
12,345,679 x 5l = 629,629,629 Totals 51
12,345,679 x 78 = 962,962,962

Note: The middle multiple in each group equals the sum of the digits of any one result in that group.

The sum of all multiples in brackets equals the sum of all the digits of the results either across or up and down in that group.

For example: 33 in the second group equals the sum of all the digits in any 9 digit number in that group, as 407,407,407. The sum of all the 27 digits in this group equals the sum of the 3 multipliers, that is, the sum of 6, 33 and 60.

THINK OF A CARD!

Here's what the world's been waiting for – a cardless card trick. All you need do is ask someone to think of any card in the deck, giving the value of 11 to a Jack, 12 to a Queen, 13 to a King and 1 to an Ace. Now you will guarantee in only one quick trick to tell him of what card he's thinking.

Here's the technique:

1. Think of a card.

2. Now add the number of the card next higher in sequence. (If he's thinking of a King 13, add Ace = 1, = 14.)

3. Multiply the result by 5.

4. Now recall to him the old auction bridge value of the suits: Clubs, 6 – Diamonds, 7 – Hearts, 8 – Spades, 9; and tell him to add the value of the suit to his total.

5. Ask for his result.

6. Mentally deduct 5, and tell him the card he thought of.

Example:

Suppose he thinks of the 10 of Hearts.............................. 10

1. He adds the next card higher in sequence.................... 11
   21
2. Multiply by 5.. 5
   105
3. Add the suit value (Hearts = 8) 8
   113
4. As soon as you hear 113, subtract 5.......................... – 5
   And you get 108. 108

The first figure (10) tells you the card he was thinking of. The second figure (8) shows you the suit (Hearts) it was.

TRICK MATHEMATICS

Ask a spectator to write down or say rapidly any number formed by three identical numbers. (Stress or emphasize the word "three".) Law of average usually results in s/he will say or write 333. Now you have already written down on a calling card or paper 333. Show this and say that you predicted that s/he would have picked that number. If not, don't worry.

Have him/her add up the three figures and divide the number by that answer. You then take out from your pocket and find the number you had previously written: 37.

No matter what number of 3 identical figures, he result is always the same – 37. If 555 ÷ 15 = 37; 777 ÷ 21 = 37, etc. Try it! Had 333 been chosen, then you made two successful predictions.

Someone asked me to review Trigonometry

Let's take a stab at it. They have terms called functions, and these are always abbreviated. If you have a friend named Theodore, you call him Ted, right? We keep Trig to 3-letter names!

Sine is **sin,** don't look at me. It's in the book! Cosine, what else, **cos**; Tangent, hey, **tan**; Cosecant, **csc**; Secant, **sec**; lastly, Cotangent, **cot**.

In Geometry, angles are in degrees, 45°, 20°, etc. Now angles are **Radians**, which use π to tell the measure of the angle. For the record, 2π is the measure of a Circle = 360°; or π radians = 180°. But in Trig you use Radians and Angles.

The values of Sin, Cos, and Tan in the triangle below show their relationship to one another.

Value of **sine** of the angle *0* is **side opposite *0* (y) divided by hypotenuse (y) of triangle.** Expressed as formula it is:

$$\sin 0 = \frac{\text{opposite}}{\text{hypotenuse}} \quad \frac{y}{h}$$

Value of **cosine** of the angle *0* is **side adjacent to *0* (x) divided by hypotenuse (y) of triangle**. Formula would be:

$$\cos 0 = \frac{\text{adjacent}}{\text{hypotenuse}} \quad \frac{x}{h}$$

Value of **tangent** of angle *0* is **side opposite *0* (y) divided by the side adjacent (x) to *0* of triangle. Formula would be:**

$$\tan 0 = \frac{\text{opposite}}{\text{adjacent}} \quad \frac{y}{x}$$

There is a short way to remember who is who:

SOH – sine opposite hypotenuse;
CAH – cosine adjacent hypotenuse;
TOA – tangent opposite adjacent.

Csc, Sec and Cot stand for **Cosecant, Secant** and **Cotangent.** And what are they but reciprocals of the other guys. For instance:

$$\csc 0 = \frac{1}{\sin 0}$$

$$\sec 0 = \frac{1}{\cos 0}$$

$$\cot 0 = \frac{1}{\tan 0}$$

CALCULUS is not a disease!

Calculus – (Latin, calculus, "a pebble", a counting device used by the old folks back in Nero's tie, and even earlier) – also any of different ways to use mathematics. Any system used in calculation.

One dominant version is of that much importance it is always referred to as just "Calculus". Calculus comes in different types: Differential, Integral, and Infinitesimal – all properly used with more advanced or higher mathematics. Don't seize up and shudder when you hear the teacher say, "Today, we start Calculus!"

It's not higher math, it's just a step higher than algebra, and geometry. The old boys of ancient days could only go so far when tallying quantities. **Arithmetic** took in the science of using numbers to compute numbers. Along came **Algebra,** another new science. which used symbols, or letters, x, y, and z. These were used to represent unknown values or again quantities. But if a quantity or something was in motion and was also a variable quantity, then **Calculus** was created.

Calculus is the science of using symbols to represent variable quantities. If there is change with this quantity, then Calculus does it all. So you see the progression: Algebra can solve special problems not permissible in Arithmetic. Calculus takes over from Algebra when things get to be unsolved. Are you still there? Please grunt or something! Thank you!

Let's show some steps in this calculating trio. **Arithmetic:** Five apple growers dump their apples together, with an agreement to divide evenly after a harvest. 926 bushels are weighed in, so how much do I get? True we don't see the result right away, so we use division! and we each get 185-1/5 bushels.

Algebra: If it takes one man to dig a canal in 6 days, while it take another man 7 days to do another identical canal, how long would it take if they both went at it together? By no means can arithmetic solve this one. So we try algebra. A simple algebraic equation ($1/6 + 1/7 = 1/x$) is the answer for which we're looking: 3 and 3/13 days.

Calculus. A navy ship is sailing east in a dense fog at 3 knots per hour, and a second ship is sailing north at 4 knots per hour. The first boat will pass in front of the second with 5 miles between them. How much later will the two boats be closest to one another?

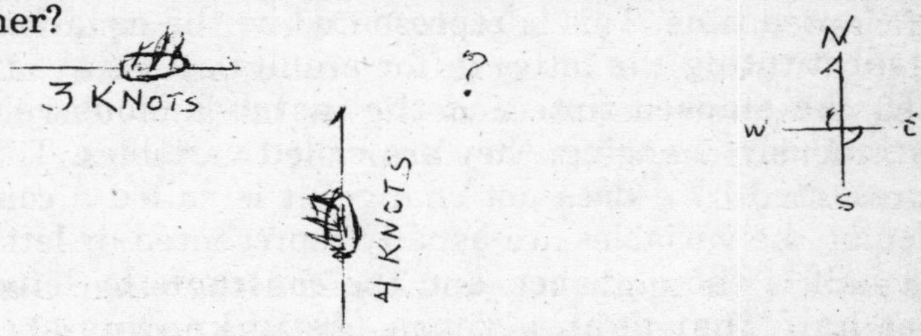

Since the positions of the two ships are constantly changing, calculus, the mathematics of variable quantities, includes the methods required to solve this problem. The solution is as follows. First, an equation is set up (by algebra) expressing the distance between the two ships at any time. Second, an equation is derived (by calculus) for the rate of variation of this distance. Now it is apparent that the distance between the ships decreases for a time, and then starts increasing. In between, there must be that instant when the distance neither decreases nor increases, and this must be the instant when the two ships are closest together. Therefore, thirdly, the expression for the rate of variation is set equal to zero, and fourth, and finally, this last equation is solved by algebra.

The only new step in this process, therefore, for the person who knows algebra, is finding a mathematical expression for rate of variation. This is done by a Calculus operation known as differentiation.

DEFINITIONS and ELEMENTARY OPERATIONS

Some of the fundamental concepts of the calculus can be easily illustrated by a simple problem of acceleration. When a body falls, Newton's laws of physics state that it accelerates, i.e., that its velocity increases continuously, at the rate of 32 feet per second each second.

Thus, at the end of the first second, the body is falling at the rate of 32 feet per second; at the end of the second second, it is moving at 64 feet per second; and at the end of the third second, it has reached a velocity of 96 feet per second. The magnitude of the velocity depends on the length of time of fall, or, in the terminology of calculus, the velocity is a function of the elapsed time. This is represented by the equation $v = 32\ t$, or, substituting the letter g (for gravity), $v = gt$. As the body falls, the elapsed time and the instantaneous velocity are continuously changing; they are called variables. The number represented by g does not change; it is called a constant. In calculus the variables are usually represented by letters in the last half of the alphabet, and the constants by letters in the first half, just as in algebra the unknowns are usually represented by x, y, or z and the knowns by a, b, or c.

Although the velocity and the time are changing, it is possible to find a constant mathematical expression for the amount of acceleration, which is the rate of variation of the one as it depends on the rate of variation of the other. For this purpose, a minute increment of time is added to one side of the equation, and the corresponding minute increment of velocity is added to the other. This is expressed by the equation $v + \Delta v = g\ (t + \Delta t)$, in which Δv and Δt (read "delta v" and "delta t", respectively) are a minute increment of velocity and a corresponding minute increment of time, respectively. This equation may now be solved, by the methods of algebra, as follows:

$$v + \Delta v = g(t + \Delta t)$$

$$v + \Delta v = gt + g\Delta t$$

but $$v = gt$$

therefore $$\Delta v = g\Delta t$$

and $$\frac{\Delta v}{\Delta t} = g$$

It should be noted that Δv does not mean Δ times v; the Δ is an ***operator***, like the arithmetical signs + or $\sqrt{\ }$, and the expression Δv simply means "a minute increment of v".

The ratio $\frac{\Delta v}{\Delta t}$ is evidently the acceleration, the rate of variation of velocity. However, the problem is not always so simple. When the equation is solved for the ratio of increments, the right-hand side of the equation may also contain increments, which introduces a further complication. For example, the distance that the body has fallen is equal to the average velocity multiplied by the time: $s = v_{av}t$, in which s equals the distance and v_{av}. equals the average velocity. The average velocity is evidently the average between zero, the initial velocity, and v, the final velocity; hence, $v_{av} = 1/2gt$; and so the equation for distance as a function of time becomes $s = 1/2gt^2$. To find the rate of variation of distance, minute increments are added as before:

$$s = \frac{1}{2}gt^2$$

$$s + \Delta s = \frac{1}{2}g(t + \Delta t)^2$$

$$s + \Delta s = \frac{1}{2}g(t^2 + 2t\Delta t + (\Delta t)^2)$$

$$s + \Delta s = \frac{1}{2}gt^2 + gt\Delta t + \frac{1}{2}g(\Delta t)^2$$

$$\Delta s = gt\,\Delta t + \frac{1}{2}g(\Delta t)^2$$

$$\frac{\Delta s}{\Delta t} = gt + \frac{1}{2}g\Delta t$$

In order to reduce this equation to a convenient form, the minute increments are made to become increasingly smaller, until finally they become infinitesimal increments (hence the name infinitesimal calculus); these infinitesimal increments are called ***differentials*** and are represented by a variable preceded by the letter d, as ds or dt. Like Δ, d is an operator, that is, a symbol of an operation

$$\frac{ds}{dt} = gt + \frac{1}{2}gdt$$

Although ds and dt are both infinitely small, the ratio $\frac{ds}{dt}$ is still finite, and is equal to gt, for the additional quantity $1/2\, gdt$ is so small as to be negligible. This is the essential technique of calculus: evaluating the finite ratio of two very infinitesimal quantities, and neglecting any quantities infinitesimal in comparison with finite quantities. This finite ratio is called a ***derivative***, and the process of elaborating a derivative is called ***differentiation.***

The mathematician does not actually go through this elaborate process each time he solves a calculus problem; there are about a dozen formulae, one or more of which will suffice for the differentiation of any algebraic function.

It is now possible to return to the original problem and understand the solution. The diagram represents the position of the two boats at t hours after the first boat has passed directly in front of the second. According to the first step, the algebraic equation for the distance between the two boats is simply the length of the hypotenuse of the triangle:

$$x = \sqrt{(3t)^2 + (5 - 4t)^2}$$

$$= \sqrt{25t^2 - 40 + 25}$$

The derivative of this function (second step) is

$$\frac{dx}{dt} \quad \frac{1}{2} \; \frac{50 - 40}{\sqrt{25t^2 - 40t + 25}}$$

The third step is to set this function equal to zero:

$$\frac{1}{2} \; \frac{50t - 40}{\sqrt{25t^2 - 40t + 25}}$$

The fourth step is to solve this equation by algebra:

$$50t - 40 = 0$$
$$50t = 40$$
$$t = \frac{4}{5}$$

That is, the boats will be closest 4/5 of an hour, or 48 minutes, later. The distance at this time can be found from the equation of the first step – 3 miles.

Now well glance over a refresh of INTEGRAL CALCULUS. The infinitesimal calculus is divided into two branches: differential calculus and integral calculus. The problem of the two boats is solved by means of differential calculus; a function is given, and the mathematician must differentiate it. In the integral calculus, the derivative is given, and the mathematician must find the function corresponding to it. This process, the inverse of differentiation, is called ***integration.***

The actual applications of integral calculus to the solution of problems are far more frequent than the applications of differential calculus. For example, in any problem involving variable motion, velocity may be expressed as a variation in distance with respect to time, and the equation for velocity may be written $v = dx/dt$ in which x is distance and t is time. In the problem of the falling body discussed above, the laws of physics state that the velocity increases at the rate of 32 feet per second each second; or, in algebraic language, $v = 32t$. Therefore $dx/dt = 32t$. This equation is called a differential equation; the solution of differential equations by means of integration as a first step p and algebra as a second step is the most important operation in calculus. The equation may be rewritten: $dx = 32tdt$, and its solution indicated by

$$x = \int 32tdt$$

in which the symbol $\int$ is to be read "the integral of" just as the symbol d is to be read "the differential of". The solution of this differential equation is $x = 16t^2$ or $x = 1/2gt^2$. In this way one may prove, by means of calculus, what t was before merely an assumption: that the average velocity is one half the final velocity.

HISTORY OF CALCULUS.

Although the integral calculus appears to be more complicated, historically it was developed prior to the differential calculus. Integration can be regarded as the summation (hence the symbol $\int$, a modified S, for *sum*) of an infinitely large number of infinitely small quantities. This type of summation was essentially the method used by the German astronomer Johannes Kepler in determining the areas of the orbits of the planets, about 1612. Similar methods of integration, and operations equivalent to what is now called differentiation. were performed by Pierre de Fermat, and later by Isaac Barrow. The calculus in essentially its now present form was developed independently by Isaac Newton, a pupil of Barrow, and by Gottfried Wilhelm Leibnitz. Newton called his method, which he developed about 1666, the calculus of fluxions. He used the symbol x for the derivative which we now write dx/dt Leibnitz developed his infinitesimal calculus about 1675, using essentially the modern notation. Commencing about 1699, a great dispute arose as to the priority of the discovery. The situation was complicated by the fact that neither Newton nor Leibnitz had ever published their works, and by fierce selfish pride, Newton personally took no part in the controversy, which was carried on long after the death of Leibnitz in 1716. One result of the dispute was that the British mathematicians continued for about a century to use the Newtonian notations while all the continental mathematicians used the Leibnitzian.

Great advances in the applications of the calculus, and in methods of differentiation and integration, were made during the early 18th century by Jacob Bernoulli, Johann Bernoulli, Alexis Clairaut, and Leonhard Euler. These men showed the power of calculus, developed its applications to a number of problems, fitted calculus into its proper place among such other branches of mathematics as trigonometry and geometry, and developed a useful notation. At this time calculus met difficulties with philosophers and such religious leaders as Bishop George Berkeley. These men charged that infinitely small quantities were meaningless and that calculus at best achieved correct results by a compensation of errors; they ridiculed quantities which were between somethings and nothings. Nonetheless, calculus did supply correct answers to otherwise insoluble problems, and it continued to flourish. The critics were finally silenced by the introduction of the concept of "limit": the differential is not really to be thought of as an infinitely small quantity, but the derivative is to be considered as the limit approached by the ratio of two differentials, as the differentials approach more and more closely to infinitesimal magnitude. This change in definition in no way affected the solutions and results achieved by calculus.

Further progress in the development of calculus during the 18th century was made by Jean d'Alembert, J. L. Lagrange, and Daniel Bernoulli, and at the close of the century by Pierre de Laplace. These men further developed the applications of calculus, elaborated new methods for solving various types of differential equations, and produced complete and consistent developments of such entire sciences as mechanics and probability. Early in the 19th century A. L. Cauchy showed how to solve most of the important remaining problems of integration. Since that time few important developments have been made in calculus itself, though calculus has been used in virtually every important mathematical advance. Note: Take time to review the lives of the many mathematicians and sciences mentioned above. They all make great reading.)

Don't Quit!

When things go wrong, as they sometimes will,
When the road you're trudging seems all uphill,
When the funds are low and the debts are high,
And you want to smile, but you have to sigh,
When care is pressing you down a bit,
Rest, if you must, but don't you quit.

Life is queer with its twists and turns,
As everyone of us sometimes learns,
And many a failure turns about,
When he might have won had he stuck it out;
Don't give up though the pace seems slow –
You may succeed with another blow.

Success is failure turned inside out –
The silver tint in the clouds of doubt,
And you never can tell how close you are,
It may be near when it seems so far;
So stick to the fight when you're hardest hit –
It's when things seem worst that you must not quit!

– Anon E. Mouse

AND ON STAGE RIGHT
THE "MATH MASTER"!

Chapter 15

AN AMAZING MATH-E-MAGICS MEMORY TRICK!

With this trick at your command, you can get a reputation for memory as good as Macauley's. Your reputation will be thoroughly undeserved.

In the table below, you will see 49 key numbers with 7-figure numbers below them. Tell the spectators you know every total by heart. "Give me the key number, and I'll tell you the number below it."

Ask anyone to select a number in the circle, and offer to tell him the seven-figure number beneath it.

You must admit that this will be quite a substantial memory stunt – that is, if it involved any memory at all.

23	**39**	**18**	**22**	**4**	**38**	**16**
4370774	0550550	9213471	3369549	5167303	9437077	7291011
2	**45**	**30**	**34**	**25**	**6**	**15**
3145943	6516730	1459437	5493257	6392134	7189763	6280886
9	**37**	**46**	**3**	**1**	**17**	**32**
0224606	8426842	7527965	4156178	2134718	8202246	3471897
21	**5**	**44**	**11**	**41**	**19**	**8**
2358314	6178538	5505505	2246066	2572910	0336954	9101123
29	**12**	**33**	**13**	**43**	**7**	**10**
0448202	3257291	4482022	4268426	4594370	8190998	1235831
49	**14**	**24**	**47**	**26**	**40**	**28**
0662808	5279651	5381909	8538190	7303369	1561785	9325729
31	**27**	**35**	**48**	**20**	**42**	**36**
2460662	8314594	6404482	9549325	1347189	3583145	7415617

But here is how it's done:

1. Add 11 to the number selected.

2. Reverse the result.

3. This number represents the 1st two numbers of the trick. Keep adding the two previous numbers, leaving out the 10's.

Example:

Suppose the victim chooses **32.**

1. You add **11** and get **43.**

2. Reverse this **43** and you have the first two figures in your final answer – **34**.

3. Add the 3 and 4 and you get 7.

4. Add the 7 and 4 and get 11. (Omit 10 – just put down the 1.)

5. The next figure is the 1 plus the 7, which is 8.

6. The next figure is the 8 plus 1 which is 9.

7. The next figure is the 9 plus 8, which is 17. (Just put down figure 7.)

This naturally produces the number.

You can make up a table of your own, using this principle and carrying out the numbers to as many places as you wish.

Remember: the more credit you get for your remarkable memory, the less you deserve. *Remember,* let them pick the 2-digit heading number, and you tell them all that you can *remember* any sequence on that card. Now that's a great memory! ***You'll be in their thoughts from then on.***

TELE-PHONEY!

This is really two tricks in one. Once you have mastered the first, you will be able to do the second over the telephone if the mood strikes you.

Like most math-e-magical stunts, this one appears complicated, but is really quite simple. All you need do is pay close attention to the directions. You can master the routine in no time.

Tell your friend to write down any digit from 1 to 9, inclusive. Then direct him as follows:

1. Stick a cipher (zero) to the right of the digit he wrote down.

2. Add the original digit.

3. Multiply the result by 3.

4. Multiply this result by 11.

5. Multiply the final result by 3.

6. Then ask him to tell you the last digit of his answer.

You can then tell him his complete answer. It is all very simple. The answer is always in four digits.

When he tells you the last digit of his answer, all you need do is subtract it from 9, and you have the second digit of his answer.

The first digit will always be one more than the second digit.

The third digit will be the first digit subtracted from nine.

Stock Brokers in the Crowd?

Everyone should know this rule, particularly those dealing in stocks. With a little practice one will find that he or she can do most interest problems mentally and without the use of pencil and paper.

1. Place decimal point in the principal three places to left.

2. Multiply number of days by rate of interest.

Now if the rate multiplied by the number of days equals 36, it is exactly 1/1000 of the principal – which is the same as placing the decimal point three places to the left.

For example:

Principal $1,200.00, rate 6%.

Days	Rate	Rate x Days	Principal	Interest
6	6 %	36	$1200	$1.20
9	4 %	36	1200	1.20
8	4-1/2 %	36	1200	1.20
9	8 %	72 twice 36	1200	2.40
6	3 %	18 half of 36	1200	.60
12	4-1/2%	54 = 1/2 x 36	1200	1.80
30	6 %	180 = 5 x 36	1200	6.00

Where your rate multiplied by the days equals a fraction, for example, 7 days at 5-1/2% would be 37-1/2. Figure 7 days at 6% which is 42 (which is 1-1/6 of 36 or 1-1/6 of the principal). This will give you the amount of interest at 6%. Now 5-1/2% is 1/12 less than 6%; therefore subtract 1/12 of the 6% results from the 6% result. This will give you the interest for 7 days at 5-1/2%.

Another Short Cut method for computing the 6% Interest: –

The interest for one year on any principal at 6% is .06 of the principal. For one month it is 1/12 of .06 or .005 of the principal. For six days it is 1/5 of .005 or .001 of the principal. For one day it is 1/6 of .001 or .000 1/6 of the principal.

Put into more concise form, we have:

Int. for 1 year = .06 of Prin.
Int. for 1 mo. = .005 of Prin.
Int. for 6 days = .001 of Prin.
Int. for 1 day = .000 1/6 of Prin.

Problem:

Using this method, find the interest on $1,600 for 3 years, 4 months, 24 days. (1) at 6%. (2) At 7-1/2%. (3) At 5-1/2.

Solution:

(1) Prin. = $1600
Rate = 6%
Time = 3 yr. 4 mo. 24 days.
Int. (.18 + .02 + .004) x $1600
Int = .204 x $1600 = $326.40

(2) Interest at 6% = $326.40; interest at 7-1/2% is 1/4 greater.

Solution:

Int. at 6% = $326.40
Int. at 1-1/2% $ 81.60 (1/4 of $326.40)
Int. 7-1/2% = $408.00

(3) Interest at 5-1/2% is 1/12 less than 6%

Solution:
Int. at 6% = $326.40
Int. 1/2% = – $ 27.20 = (1/12 of $326.40)
Int. at 5-1/2% = $299.20

Interest for any rate

can be easily computed by beginning with 6%.

Suppose you wanted to find the amount of interest on given principal for a specified amount of time at 3-1/2% or 2-1/2%. For 3-1/2%, we would first get the amount for 6%, as earlier shown, and we would then add one-half of this amount to 1/12 of the same amount and this would total 3-1/2%. In the case of 2-1/2%, the 1/12 of the amount would be subtracted instead of added.

For Loan of $1,000.00
Amortized over 25 years

5.00%	5.82	10.00%	8.95
5.25%	5.96	10.25%	9.12
5.50%	6.10	10.50%	9.29
5.75%	6.25	10.75%	9.46
6.00%	6.40	11.00%	9.63
6.25%	6.55	11.25%	9.80
6.50%	6.70	11.50%	9.98
6.75%	6.85	11.75%	10.15
7.00%	7.00	12.00%	10.32
7.25%	7.16	12.50%	10.50
7.50%	7.32	12.25%	10.67
7.75%	7.48	12.75%	10.85
8.00%	7.64	13.00%	11.03
8.25%	7.80	13.25%	11.21
8.50%	7.96	13.50%	11.39
8.75%	8.12	13.75%	11.56
9.00%	8.28	14.00%	11.74
9.25%	8.45	14.25%	11.92
9.50%	8.62	14.50%	12.10
9.75%	8.78	14.75%	12.29

e.g., $50,000 @ 13% = $551.50/Mo. P.&I.
(50 x 11.03 = $551.50.)

Let's Take A Special Break!

From time to time we have to multiply odd groupings. As math-e-magicians in the making, let's try out some here.

In every mental problem, it's best to have a pattern to go with the question at hand. Take 48 x 27; or a larger one, 456 x 789. Calculate in this new fashion. 48 x 27 = **1296**. 456 x 789 = **359784**. Did I hear you say: No way, man!" Bend an ear here.

1st example: 8 x 7 = 56, write 6 and carry 5; 5 plus 4 x 7 (28) plus 2 x 8 comes to 49, write 9, carry 4; 4 plus 4 x 2 = 12, write 12. Always add the carried number first.

2nd example: multiply 6 x 9; followed by 5 x 9 and 6 x 8; then the triplet: 4 x 9, 6 x 7, and the mid-section 5 x 8; keeping the cadence, 4 x 8, and 5 x 7, ending with a flourish, 4 x 7 = 359,784. Take time to swing in all these directions.

Here's a new approach to nearly whole (fractional) numbers

When you're multiplying two numbers , one of which is has a fraction, try this method. For example, 48 x 4-3/4. Go up a fraction to make the 4 now read 5. Then 48 x 5 = 240. Now subtract 1/4 of 48 = 12, giving answer of 240 – 12 = 228.

Exercise 12.A

1. 39 x 6-2/3
2. 85 x 14-4/5
3. 144 x 6-7/8
4. 125 x 7-4/5
5. 488 x 8-7/8
6. 570 x 3-9/10
7. 266 x 8-6/7
8. 828 x 4-8/9
9. 352 x 3-15/16

He who knows not and knows not that he knows not,
he is a fool – shun him;
He who knows not and knows he knows not,
he is a simple – teach him;
He who knows and knows not he knows ,
he is asleep – wake him;
He who knows and knows he knows,
follow him;

Quoted by ARISTOTLE

REMEMBER NOW... YOU CAN'T CLIMB THE LADDER OF SUCCESS IF YOU'RE LAYING DOWN ON THE JOB ALL THE TIME!
GRAY ROOTS!
SQUARE ROOTS

Chapter 16

SQUARES and SQUARE ROOTS

When we say "square this number," we immediately think "multiply it by itself."

The square of any number is that number multiplied by itself. It can also be defined as a square grid having all sides the same value as each other.

Imagine building squares by laying out pennies: the first square will have one penny: the second 4, the third 9 and so forth. Therefore, one, four, and nine are the squares.

So 4 squared is 4 x 4. It is written with a small figure ^{2} (4^2) and it is known as the second power of four. Four squared equals 16, and 4 is the square root of 16 – and is written $\sqrt{16}$.

The sequence of squares and the sequence of odd numbers have what at first sight seems a mysterious relationship:

$$1 = 1 = 1^2$$
$$1 + 3 = 4 = 2^2$$
$$1 + 3 + 5 = 9 = 3^2$$
$$1 + 3 + 5 + 7 = 16 = 4^2$$
$$1 + 3 + 5 + 7 + 9 = 25 = 5^2$$
$$1 + 3 + 5 + 7 + 9 + 11 = 36 = 6^2$$
$$1 + 3 + 5 + 7 + 9 + 11 + 13 = 49 = 7^2$$

And so on and on.

Here's a quaint array of flowing digits!

$$1 + 2 + 1 = 2^2$$

$$1 + 2 + 3 + 2 + 1 = 3^2$$

$$1 + 2 + 3 + 4 + 3 + 2 + 1 = 4^2$$

$$1 + 2 + 3 + 4 + 5 + 4 + 3 + 2 + 1 = 5^2$$

$$1 + 2 + 3 + 4 + 5 + 6 + 5 + 4 + 3 + 2 + 1 = 6^2$$

$$1 + 2 + 3 + 4 + 5 + 6 + 7 + 6 + 5 + 4 + 3 + 2 + 1 = 7^2$$

$$1 + 2 + 3 + 4 + 5 + 6 + 7 + 8 + 7 + 6 + 5 + 4 + 3 + 2 + 1 = 8^2$$

$$1 + 2 + 3 + 4 + 5 + 6 + 7 + 8 + 9 + 8 + 7 + 6 + 5 + 4 + 3 + 2 + 1 = 9^2$$

Approximating Square Roots
(Guesstimation)

Not all squares are intended to be perfect squares. Life would be very easy if they were. But from time to time in classroom work, it is necessary for you to approximate the nearest value of said square, so let's look at this short cut.

If a number is divided by your closest guess at its square root, and then you get one half of the sum of your guess and the quotient, you have a much better approximation.

Therefore, in seeking the square root of 50, your first guess would perhaps be 7+. Then divide 50 by 7 and you get 7.14+. One half of (7 + 7.14) = 7.07, and this is a much better approximation than your first guess of 7. This may be repeated for further improvement by dividing 50 by 7.07, and getting half of the sum of your divisor and quotient. Every time the procedure is repeated the square root is improved.

Another example: Suppose you are seeking the square root of 41. In order to make your first guess, you may reason like this: You know that the square of 6 is 36, and the square of 7 is 49. 41 is 5/13 of the way from 36 to 49. So your guess at the square root might be 6-5/13. Expressed decimally, 6-5/13 is approximately 6.4, so this would be your first guess.

When 41 is divided by 6.4 = 6.40625. 1/2 of (6.40000 + 6.40625) = 6.403125,which is rounded off to six places at 6.40312 (because divisor and quotient matched for three figures, namely, 6.40).

Now we repeat the procedure by dividing 41 by 6.40312, which gives a quotient of 6.403128474868...

There is agreement in six places. and this confirms your previous work, and justifies your trusting 12 figures of the new average of divisor and quotient, so the square root of 41 is 6.4031242374868. This is correct to 12 figures, and is as accurate as the old method of determining square root, (as was taught in the old grammar school) but much faster, easier to remember.

At this time let us digress for a moment!

Earlier we read about the pennies used to construct the shapes of small squares. To make up the second square we must add 3 coins to the 1 square. To make the third square, add 5, and so on. (Note: any triangle number added to the next higher triangle number always comes out a square number. 3, 6, 10, etc., as indicated earlier in that diagram.

It is an odd coincidence that if you multiply any triangle number by 8 and add 1 you come up with a square number. For example:

Triangle 1 = 1	(8 x 1)	+ 1 =	9 = 3^2
Triangle 2 = 3	(8 x 3)	+ 1 =	25 = 5^2
Triangle 3 = 6	(8 x 6)	+ 1 =	49 = 7^2
Triangle 4 = 10	(8 x 10)	+ 1 =	81 = 9^2
Triangle 5 = 15	(8 x 15)	+ 1 =	121 = 11^2
Triangle 6 = 21	(8 x 21)	+ 1 =	169 = 13^2

Note that the odd sequence of numbers 3, 5, 7, 9, 11, 15, etc., shows up once again.

Mathematicians have been fascinated by the connections between square and triangle numbers, and between ordinary numbers and numbers of special shape for centuries. They are still trying to find new connections between them.

Numbers ending in 5 can be squared mentally very easily: ignoring the 5, which is always 25, add the value of 1 to the left-hand figures: eg., square 75. Mentally, add 1 to 7 = 8. Now multiply 7 x 8 = 56 and add on 25. Answer = 5625. Square 135. (13 x (13 + 1) = 18225.

Numbers made up on1y of threes have a special pattern of squares:

$$33^2 = 1089$$
$$333^2 = 110889$$
$$3333^2 = 11108889$$
$$33333^2 = 1111088889$$
$$333333^2 = 111110888889$$

and so on.

Squares for other numbers can be found quickly by using the methods described in the section on multiplication.

Here's A Twisty Question!

Write 23 with only 2's – or 45 with only 4's, or even 1,000 with nothing but 9's.

Answer: $22 + \frac{2}{2}$, $44 + \frac{4}{4}$, $999 + \frac{9}{9}$

How brainy can you get? Try making up some twisters for your friends and pals at school.

FINDING A SQUARE ROOT

This is the usual method of finding square roots:

First divide the number into groups by putting a mark over every second figure – starting from the right with the units digit, going left to the hundreds digit, and so on. For instance, if the problem is to find the square root of 233289, set it out like this:

```
 .  .  .
232324
```

Now find the largest number the square of which is less than 23:

```
       .  .  .
      232324(482
      16
 88)  723
      704
962)  1924
      1924
```

this is 4 – which gives you the first figure of the answer. Insert this to the right of the number, and subtract 4^2 (16) from 23. Now bring down the next group of figures – 23 – and put it after the remainder just obtained to make 723.

The first part of the divisor of 723 (obtained by doubling 4, that part of the root you have already obtained) is 8. The final digit of the divisor, and the second of the root itself, is arrived at by trial. It will be the largest number that, inserted after the 8, and then used to multiply the number thus obtained, will give a product of less than 723. It turns out in this case to be 8 – for 8 x 88 = 704. and 723 – 704 = 19.

Now go through the same process again:

Bring down the next group of numbers, 24, to make 1924.

Arrive at a divisor by doubling 48 (the part of the root already arrived at). This gives you 96.

Find by trial the next number of the square root (in this case the final one), which will also be the last digit of the divisor. It turns out to be 2, and you now have the complete root, 482, which can be checked by multiplying it by itself.

Square roots by factors. Square roots can also be found by breaking numbers down into factors which are the squares of known numbers (4, 9, 16, 25, and so on). Multiplying together the square roots of the factors will then give the square root of the number.

For instance the number 20736 is found to have the factors: eg., 4 x 4 x 4 x 4 x 9 x 9. The square root is then 2 x 2 x 2 x 2 x 3 x 3, which equals 144.

Both these methods are time consuming however – and there are short cuts which, given a little practice, allow you to arrive at square roots mentally. ***First you must learn the table of squares of numbers from 1 to 9 by heart:*** Trust me!

TABLE A

Number	Square
1	1
2	4
3	9
4	16
5	25
6	36
7	49
8	64
9	81

You will see from this table that any square ending in 1 will have a root ending in 1 or 9. A square ending in 4 will have a root ending in 2 or 8. A square ending in 9 will have a root ending in 3 or 7. A square ending in 6 a root ending in 4 or 6, and a square ending in 5 a root ending in 5. So any number that is a perfect square will end in 1, 4, 9, 6, or 5, and, with the exception of 5, the final number of the square will indicate two possible values for the last digit of the square root.

This table is the basis of a quick method of finding square roots. To find the root of a four-figure number first break the number into two groups of two digits. For example 7396 breaks into 73 and 96.

Consider the group with the thousands and with the hundreds digits. We know that the square root we are looking for will have two digits – to find the first we think where 73 stands in relation to the memorized table of squares. It is less than 81 but more than 64, so the highest possible tens digit of the root is 8. We must now find the units digit of the square root. We know from our table that it must be 6 – but we have for two numbers that read 6 as the units value – 36 and 16. They give squares ending in 6. To decide which, take the number already arrived at as the first number of the root – in this case, 8; multiply it by itself plus 1= 72. If the product is ***more*** than the first two figures of the number for which you are finding the root, take the lower of the two possible digits figures – in this case 4, to arrive at the square root; if it is ***less,*** take the higher of the two possible figures: less/more would be 6 – more/less would be the 4; so 8 x (8 + 1) = 8 x 9 = 72, which is less than 73. So we take the more – 6. The square root of 7396 is therefore 86.

Here is another example.

To find the square root of 3969.

39 lies between 36 and 49, so the first figure of the square root is 6. The second figure could be 3 or 7. 6 x 7 = 42, which is more than 39 so if more/less is understood, we must take the lower of the possible units digits. The square root is then 63.

Exercise – Mental Multiplication and Factoring

Multiply mentally by 5 all the numbers in Table 1 on page 35.

Factor the numbers from 399 to 428; e.g., 399 = 3 x 133, 7 x 57, 7 x 3 x 19; 400 = 2 x 2 x 2 x 2 x 5 x 5; etc.

But What About
Real BIG Numbers?

If the square has five or six numbers, we know from experience the square root will have three. To find the square roots of numbers up to 40,000 you must remember more squares – those up to 20, at least. An easy way to remember squares to 20 is to use and review **Short Cut 60 – Boomerang Stage 1.** (See pp 5.1-5.2 and p. 22.6)

TABLE B

N + 1	NUMBER	SQUARE	DIFFERENCE OF 2
10 x 11 = 110	11	121	add 23
11 x 12 = 132	12	144	" 25
12 x 13 = 156	13	169	" 27
13 x 14 = 182	14	196	" 29
14 x 15 = 320	15	225	" 31
15 x 16 = 240	16	256	" 33
16 x 17 = 272	17	289	" 35
17 x 18 = 306	18	324	" 37
18 x 19 = 342	19	361	" 39
19 x 20 = 380	20	400	

Memorize these tables and you can set about finding the square root of longer numbers which are perfect squares. Try this example. Let's find the square root of 39204.

First divide the number into two groups of digits by taking out the last two figures. This gives:

392 04

Check the table and you'll see that 392 falls between the squares of 19 and 20 – which are 361 and 400. The first two figures of the root you are extracting will be 19 – the square root of the lower figure. To find the final figure you use the method already used: the number ends in a 4, the digit you are looking for must therefore be either a 2 or an 8. To find which, add 1 to 19 = 20 (first figures of the root) and multiply the sum by 19.

The product, 380 (19 x 20), is less than 392, so you take the higher of the two possible digits – the 8. You now have the complete square root of 39204: 198.

Let's state that rule again: Less/More. . . More/Less!!

Now try this one: Find the square root of 32041
Divide the number into two groups of digits as before:

320 41

From the table we know that 320 falls between the squares of 17 and 18. The first two digits of the square root must be 17. The number ends in 1 so the final figure must be 1 or 9. 17 x 18 = 306, this is less than 320, so you take the higher of the two possible digits to arrive at the square root of 179.

What do we do if the squared number is higher than 40000? Well, I guess, you'd have to do it another way.

As an example, to get the square root of 478864, first separate or break it up into groups of two figures, always starting from the right:

47 88 64

To find the hundreds figure of the square root go back to Table A on page 104. We see that 47 rests between the squares of 6 and 7. Always take the lower numbers as our first figure – **6**.

To find the tens figure we must find the difference between 47 and the square of 6, that is – between 47 and 36.

47 – 36 = **11**

We now put **11** before the left-hand digit of the second group of figures in the number from which we are extracting the square. This gives **118**. We divide this number by **twice the figure you have already arrived at** (6) **plus** 1 as the first in the square root: 6 x 2 = 12 + 1 = 13.

(This **13** is divided into **118**.)118 ÷ 13 = **9**, with remainder of 1.

Think of 9 as the middle number.

(note that you are obtaining the quotient (9) which will give a remainder ***above or below*** – the remainder is the number that must be added to or subtracted from the dividend to bring it to the nearest multiple of the divisor).

The quotient obtained, 9, is the tens digit of the square root we are extracting, so the first two digits of the root are 69.

We know that the units digit must be 8 or 2, for the number ends in a 4. **As the quotient obtained, 9, was greater than remainder, 1,** we **take the smaller** of the two possible figures arrive at the complete square root of 692.

When the quotient is equal to or smaller than the remainder, take the larger of the two possible figures as the units digit.

Memorize: **LESS IS MORE; MORE IS LESS**. Once you understand that rule, you've got it licked!

EXERCISE 12. B – Find square roots:

1. 21025 **2.** 35721 **3.** 44944 **4.** 15376 **5.** 35344
6. 39601 **7.** 20449 **8.** 40401 **9.** 34969 **10.** 8836 **(1/2 of 5!)**

Look at a Number and Square it in Your Head!

Quite recently, I've become intrigued in a new method of squaring any seemingly complex large number. There's nothing complex about digits from 0 to 9, but the method I've come up with for doing squares is unique. At least I think so.

Someone says, "OK, let's see you square 48795 without a Calculator. Yeah, show us!" With that they ream off five numbers. (Now you've done it! Where do I go from here?)

Simple, as long as you can multiply up to a 100. Square any figure from 2 to 9? No sweat. Add two or three numbers consecutively? No problem! Multiply a large number (under 150) by 2? It's a possibility! So what's the big deal? Let's go!

Square 69. In your mind, assign the letters *a, b, c, d, e, f,* etc., to any length of number. Now comes the easy part. If it's a 2-figure number, 69, think of the letters ***a*** over 6; ***b*** over 9.

For example: a b
6 9

Step 1 – Square b – think 9^2 -> 81 carry 8 write **1**,
Step 2 – Cross multiply (mentally) or 2 x *ab*
2 (6 x 9) = 2(54) = 108 + remainder 8 = 116. write **6**
(remainder (rem) 11)
Step 3 – a^2 = (6 x 6) = 36 + rem 11 = **47**. Answer = **4761.**

Stage Calculator "Supreme"!!

48763^2: Here's a challenge! *Can you do this in 74 seconds!*

In your thoughts, place " *a b c d e* " in their respective places. But let us rearrange the figuring a bit, the easier way:

a b c d e
4 8 7 6 3 remainder —> (r)

e^2 = 3 x 3 = **9** **9**
2(*de*) = 2(6 x 3) = (2 x 18) = 3**6** (r 3) **6**
2(*ce*) + d^2 = 2(7 x 3) + 6^2 = 42 + 36 = 78 + 3 = 8**1** (r 8) **1**
2(*be*) + 2(*cd*) = 2(8 x 3) + 2(7 x 6) =
(2 x 24) + (2 x 42) = 48 + 84 = 132 + r 8 = 14**0** (r 14) **0**
2(*ae*) + 2(*bd*) + c^2 = 2(4 x 3) + 2(8 x 6) + 7^2 = (2 x 12) +
(2 x 48) + 49 = 24 + 96 + 49 = 169 + r 14 = 18**3** (r 18) **3**
2(*ad*) + 2(*bc*) = 2(4 x 6) + 2(8 x 7) = (2 x 24) +
(2 x 56) = 48 + 112 = 160 + r 18 = 17**8** (r 17) **8**
2(*ac*) + b^2 = 2(4 x 7) + 8^2 = (2 x 28) + 64 =
56 + 64 + 17 = 13**7** (r 13) **7**
2(*ab*) = 2(4 x 8) = (2 x 32) = 64 + r 13 = 7**7** (r 7) **7**
a^2 = 4^2 = 16 + r 7 = 23 **23**

Answer: 48763^2 = **2,377,830,169** – *Thought you'd like it!*

All Squares can be plotted using the formula above. The multiplying and adding is a good exercise for your mental breadth and depth. Try this at every spare moment. Great success in stage calculations. You'll be a whiz kid. I mean it!

Try every size of square from 2-wide to 6-wide. It's fantastic!

LOGARITHMS

When you talk of Logarithms you think of it as a high wall covered with strange powers. Well, the word "powers" is true, but "strange" it doesn't have to be.

First, it is a number written as a superscript (similar to the position that the small number to the top right hand side of 89^2 takes to mean square 89). Superscripts express the power to which a fixed number (called the 'Base') must be raised to result in another or third number.

In an expression $c^x = N$, for instance, if c is the base and equals 10, and N is a number equal to 100, then x is equal to 2 and is represented as being the logarithm of 100 to the base 10. This is written as: log 100 = 2 (signifying that "logarithm to the base 10".)

Explaining it another way, "log 100 = 2" expresses the result that 10^2, or 10 squared = 100.

Logarithms are used in simplifying multiplication and division problems, and are employed by being looked up in tables. Recently, the *calculator* – (gosh, I hate using that word) – is programmed for all these functions. The word "logarithm" literally means "reckoning number".

–o– o–o–o–o–

EXERCISE 13

Using the technique on Page **16**.5, find the square roots of these:

1. 223729 **2.** 343396 **3.** 207936 **4.** 962361 **5.** 346921
6. 529984 **7.** 278941 **8.** 746496 **9.** 7430444 **10.** 996004

Now try these same figures using Table A, page **16**.6, and Table B on page **16**.8. There are more methods than the old fashioned way. These only work for pure squares. But if guesstimation is required, this serves as a short cut to the final answer. Keeps your mind sharp as a razor.

Al Einstein and His Relative Itzak

Einstein was thrashing about with a theory: "If two observers that are in motion in respect to each other, then neither will agree that each seeing a thing happen will not agree on the exact time, or simultaneously, that the action happened, or something." "Why?" he said to himself, "may be they didn't agree on the distances between themselves. If they can't agree on the time, nor the distance, then there's trouble, big trouble, right here in Zurich River City!", as the song goes.

Einstein bounced his new ideas off his Uncle Itzak, the janitor at the University where Albert worked. "Itty," Al always called his uncle "Itty", because he was a small, "Ittyy-Bitty Uncle"; he berated him behind his back. Anyway, he said to his uncle, "Itty, the velocity of light is independent on the motion of the observer. Again, no physical body has the speed of light, understand? Now if two observers at rest to one another could agree on the distance and time between two events while observers in motion with respect to each other will not!" Itzak blinked at Albert and shook his head. "Such a relative! My brother's offspring has sproinged his cog!"

A while later, Itzak came back to the lab, interrupting Einstein, who wheeled around impatiently, "Now, what's it is?" Itzak said, "A Mr. Tooze to see you, Al." "Not now, Itzak, later. *Who* is it?"

"A man from Canada. It's a Mr. Tooze to see you." Einstein, always making cryptic notes so no one could steal his ideas, wrote in large letters, "Tooze's to see MrE!" Only Al always wrote in reverse: so he printed "ErM C22", in code.

Al sweated all afternoon on his theory and was ready to explode, when he looked up and saw in his overhead mirror the note that Itzak had mentioned. "Ach! It's a miracle! My dreams are answered! Gootenhimmel! Of course, $E=MC^2$, mine own uncle's message!" So Einstein got a Nobel prize when he put in his new ideas to the University. He wrote the heading of his findings as "The Theory of Relative Itty", but some dumb secretary thought he meant "Einstein's Theory of Relativity" instead. Itzak cleaned up too, he got a new mop, and Al slipped his wife half the loot! She was also a smart cookie!

Meet the
MATH GREATS
SO WHO'D
YOU EXPECT..
EINSTEIN?

Chapter 17

Meet the Stage Calculators – the MATH GREATS!!

The ability to do arithmetic rapidly in one's head seems to have only a moderate relationship with general intelligence and less with mathematical rationale, insight and even creativity. Some of the most excelled mathematicians have had trouble making change in the corner store, and many professional "lightning calculators" have been really quite ordinary "nerds". Very dull with regards to all other mental liabilities.

Solomon W. Golomb often astounded his friends by evaluation in his head complicated expressions in combinatorial analysis. "The number of constants one need store in the memory," he wrote, "and the number of simple rules, is far smaller than it seems." His greatest demonstrations occurred when he was a college freshman. A biology teacher had just finished explaining to the class that there was 24 pairs of human chromosomes, therefore 2^{24} ways to select one member from each parent in the formation of an egg or sperm cell. "Thus from one parent," he said, "the number of different possible germ cells 2^{24}, and you all know what that comes to."

To this rhetorical question, Golomb immediately called out "Yes, it's 16,777,216." The teacher laughed, looked down at his lecture notes, said, "Well, the actual value is . . . ," gulped, then demanded to know how Golomb had known it. Golomb replied that it was "obvious." The class immediately christen him "Einstein," and for the rest of the year several people, including the lab instructor, thought that was his name.

How did Golomb know it? He had recently memorized the values of n^n as far as $n = 10$. While the teacher was formulating his question, Golomb realized that $2^{24} = 8^8$, a number on his short list.

Contemporary lightning calculators do not make the headlines they once did in the nineteenth century, but possibly there are a few still kicking around in show biz. Georgia-born Willis Nelson Dysart, who used the stage name "Willie the Wizard," was best known in the United States. In Europe, the French performer, Maurice Dagbert, was probably the most active, but information is scanty concerning the stage calculators abroad.

Even the greatest of the lightning calculators discussed in the last chapters regularly included in their stage acts such feats as cube-root extraction and the calendar trick, which appear enormously difficult but actually are not, and many lesser calculators were not above introducing feats that operate almost entirely by trickery. Some of these tricks are so easily learned that the reader who wishes to amaze and confound his friends can master them with a minimum of practice and only the most elementary of calculating skills. Check your libraries.

Consider, for example, the following multiplication trick, surprisingly little known even though it goes back to an Italian book of 1747, *I giochi numerici: fatti arcani* (NUMERICAL GAMES: Arcane Pacts), by G. A. Alberti. The trick works with numbers of any length, but it is best to limit it to three-digit numbers unless a pocket calculator is handy for checking results. And we don't need calculators now, do we? Naw!

Ask for any number with three digits. Suppose you are given 487. Write it twice on the blackboard or on a sheet of paper:

487   487

Ask for another three-digit number. Write it under the 265 on the left. Now you need a different three-digit number as a multiple on the right. It has to be (although your audience must not know this) the "9 complement" of the multiplier on the left; that is, corresponding digits of the two multipliers must add to 9. Assume that the left multiplier is 265. The right multiplier must be 734: 2 + 7, 6 + 3, 5 + 4, all equal 9.

487   487
265   734

If you do the trick for a group, plan ahead for a friend to act as a sort of secret confederate and suggest the correct second multiplier. (Sneaky, but that's show biz!) Or write it yourself as though you were listening and putting down a number shouted at random by the audience. Announce that you now intend to perform the two multiplications in your head, add the two products and, as a grand final gesture, double the results.

Obtain the sum of the two products instantly by subtracting 1 from the multiplicand and then appending the complement. In this case 487 minus 1 is 486, the 9 complement of 486 is 513, and so the sum of the two products is 486,513. If you wrote this down, someone might notice that began with the same two digits as the multiplicand, which would look suspicious, so you conceal the fact by doubling the number.

This is not hard to do mentally, writing the digits from right to left as you perform the necessary doubling in your mind. If you prefer, you can mentally add a zero to 486,513 and divide by 5 (since multiplying by 10 and dividing by 5 is the same as multiplying by 2), in which case you write the final answer left to right. Answer will be: 973,026. Now it's well hidden!

Why does the trick work? The sum of the two products is the same as the product of 487 and 999, which in turn is the same as multiplying 487 by 1,000 and subtracting 487. Do this paper and you will see at once why the result has to be 486 followed by its 9 complement.

A much subtler principle underlies a variety of lightning-multiplication tricks involving certain curious numbers that seems innocent enough but actually can be multiplied quickly by any number of equal or shorter length.

Suppose the stage calculator asks for a nine-digit number and a confederate in the audience calls out 142,857,143. Another nine-digit number is requested and given legitimately. The performer multiplies the two numbers in his head, writing the mammoth product slowly from left to right.

The secret is absurdly simple. Merely divide the second number through twice by 7. If there is a remainder after the first division, carry it back to the front of the first digit, then divide through a second time. Supposing the second number is 123,456,789. In effect, what you must now do is divide 7 into 123,456,789,123,456,789. The result, 17,636,684,160,493,827, is the answer. The division must come out even; otherwise you know you have made a mistake.

The magic number 142,857,143 is just as easily multiplied by a number of shorter length. Merely add enough zeros at the end to make it a nine-digit number when you do the first mental division by 7. Thus if the multiplier were 123,456, you would, in your mind, divide 123,456,000,123,456 by 7. While you are writing the answer you are of course secretly looking at the multiplier and performing the mental division.

The number 142,857,143 was well known to the great stage calculators. One of the last of them to give vaudeville performances in the U.S. was the Indiana-born Arthur F. Griffith, who died in 1911 at the age of 31. He billed himself as *"Marvelous Griffith"* and had the reputation of being able to multiply two nine-digit numbers in less than half a minute. An eyewitness account of his performance in 1904, before a group of students and faculty members at the University of Indiana, follows:

Griffith, the account says, wrote the number 142,857,143 on the blackboard. A professor was asked to put a nine-digit multiplier below it. As soon as he started to write it, from left to right, *Marvelous Griffith* began to write the product from left to right. "The student audience," the account continues, "rose with a shout." Griffith wrote a small book about his methods, The Easy and Speedy Reckoner (published in Goshen, Ind., in 1901), but it says nothing about 142,857,143.

There is one danger in using 142,857,143. If the multiplier happens to be evenly divisible by 7, the product "stutters"; that is, a series of numbers will be repeated in the answer and that will arouse suspicion. The performer take a chance, knowing if the odds are much in his favour, that the number will not be a stutter, and if it does, that the audience won't notice it. If he wants no stuttering, he mentally divides the multiplier by 2.

If there is no remainder (hence a stutter) he can do any of several things. He can announce that, to make the feat even more incredible, he will reverse the multiplier, taking its digits in backward order, betting that the reversal is not a multiple of 7. Better still, he asks the audience to further randomize the multiplier by altering one of its digits.

To avoid a stutter, **Wallace Lee,** a magician who invented many excellent mathematical tricks, **devised the magic number 2,857,143.** (It is the other number with its first two digits removed.) Ask for a seven-digit multiplier in which each digit is not less than 5. This, you explain, is to make the problem more difficult; actually it simplifies the procedure.

The method is the same as before except that the entire multiplier must be doubled before you make the first division by 7. If all the digits are greater than 4, the doubling can be done in your head as you go along, digit by digit, in the following manner.

Assume that the multiplier is 8,965,797. Double the first digit, 8, and add 1, making 17. Seven goes into 17 twice, so you write 2 as the first digit of the answer, **keeping the remainder, 3,** in mind. Double the next number, 9, and add 1, making 19.

Discard the first digit (**1** of **1**9) and **substitute the 3** that was the previous remainder, making **3**9. Seven goes into 39 five times, so write 5 as the second digit of the answer, **keeping the remainder, 4, in mind.** Double the next number, 6, and add 1, making 13. Substitute 4 for the 1, making 43.

Seven goes into 43 six times, so write 6 as the third digit of the answer and keep the remainder, 1, in mind. Double the next digit, 5, and add 1, making 11. Substituting 1 for 1 leaves the same number, 11, so you divide 11 by 7, getting 1 as the fourth digit of the answer and a remainder of 4 to keep in mind.

Continue in this way until you reach the end of 8,965,797. When you double the last digit, *do not add* 1. The 2 that is the final remainder is carried back to the beginning to go in front of the 8. Now divide 28,965,797 by 7 in the ordinary manner, **without doubling.** The final result, 25,616,564,137,971, is the desired product.

The doubling procedure used for the first division is not difficult to master. The product is guaranteed not to stutter and the trick's modus operandi is much harder for the uninitiated to discover. Like the previous magic number, this one can be multiplied by smaller numbers if you mentally add zeros to the multiplier. If the digits of the multiplier are not required to be greater than 4, a good procedure is to multiply the entire number by 10 (that is, add 0 to its end), then divide through by 35. This works because 35 is the product of 7 and half of 10. Start memorizing the harder multiples of 35.

Both tricks have such gargantuan products that unless an adequate desk or pocket calculator is available it is hard to get quick confirmation of your results. ***But it looks impressive !***

There are many smaller magic numbers, however, that work less difficulty, and that are essentially the same way. For example, the product of 143 and *abc:* (in this case *abc* = 696}

To obtain a magic number in a split-second time, you can get it by dividing *abc* (696) through twice by 7 and hope that the quotient does not stutter. (The answer is: 99528.)

The product of 1,667 and *abc*: (in this case *abc* = 497) is obtained by adding a zero to *abc*0 (4970) and dividing through by 6, halving the remainder, if any (the remainder will be either 0, 2, or 4), carrying it back to the beginning and dividing *abc* (497) by 3. This is very easy to do in your head, the result will not stutter, and spectators can check the answer without a machine – all of which makes it a terrific impromptu trick to perform for friends or on stage. (answer is 828,499.)

Only reference I know to magic numbers of this type is in a privately printed work by the late Wallace Lee – (died in 1969) called *Math Miracles*, a book that contains many entertaining feats of lightning calculation. As a very pleasant exercise in number theory the reader is asked to find how the four magic numbers were obtained and why they work the way they do.

In another impressive lightning-calculation feat you ask someone to cube any number from 1 to 100 and give you the result; you quickly name the cube root. To perform this trick it is necessary to memorize only the cubes of numbers 1 through 10 (see Figure below). Notice that each cube ends in a different digit. (This is never true of squares, which explains why cube-root extraction is so much easier for a calculator than square-root extraction.) The final digit matches the cube root in every case except 2 and 8, 3 and 7. Those four exceptions are easily recalled because in each case the cube root and the final digit of the cube always add to 10.

Suppose someone calls out the cube 658,503. Discard in your mind the last three digits and consider only what is left, 658. It lies between the cubes of 8 and 9. Pick the lower of the two, 8, and call out 8 as the first digit of the answer. The terminal digit of 658,503 is 3, so you know immediately that the second digit of the cube root is 7. Call out 7. The cube root is 87.

CUBES		FIFTH POWER
1	1	100 THOUSANDS
2	8	3 MILLIONS
3	27	24 MILLIONS
4	64	100 MILLIONS
5	125	300 MILLIONS
6	216	777 MILLIONS
7	343	1 BILLION, 500 MILLIONS
8	512	3 BILLIONS
9	729	6 BILLIONS
10	1,000	10 BILLIONS

(Key for root extraction)

Stage calculators often followed this trick by asking for fifth powers of numbers. This seems even harder than giving cube roots but in fact is both easier and faster. The reason is that the Last digit of any fifth power of an integer always matches the last digit of the integer. Again, it is necessary to memorize a table (see page **17**.2). Supposing someone calls out 7,339,040,224. As soon as you hear "seven billion" you know that it lies between the 9th and the 10th number on the chart. Pick the lower number, 9. Ignore everything he says until he reaches the last digit, 4, at which point you quickly answer 94. It isn't wise to repeat this more than once or twice because it will soon become obvious that those final digits always match. Most professional calculators work with cubes and fifth powers of much larger numbers, of their choice, and by extensions of the systems shown here, but we are limited to the explanation of the simpler two-digit roots.

The Lee Calendar Trick!

Name the day of the week for any date called out! Most of the great stage calculators perform it. But to do it, you must commit to memory the table shown on page **17**.9, and **17**.13 in which a digit is associated with each month. Initial memorization can be aided by mnemonic cues shown to the right of the table.

You have to stick to these rules to calculate the day of the week. The following four-step procedure is recommended. There are other procedures and even compact formulae, but don't pay any attention to them. They're too complicated. This is the best and most carefully designed rapid mental method.

1. Consider the last two digits of the year as a single number. Divide it mentally by 12 and keep the remainder in mind. You now add three small numbers: the number of dozens, the remainder, and the number of times 4 goes into the remainder. Example: March 23, 1910. Twelve goes into 10 zero times, with a remainder of 10. Four goes into remainder 10 two times. 0 + 10 + 2 = 12. If the final result is equal to or greater than 7, divide by 7 and remember only what is left. In the example given, 12 divided by 7 has a remainder of 5. **Only the 5 is kept in the mind.** Henceforth this procedure will be called "Casting out 7's. (Mathematician would say he was using *"Modulo arithmetic"*) Modulo 7!

JAN	1	THE FIRST MONTH (1)
FEB	4	A C-O-L-D (FOUR-LETTER) MONTH
MAR	4	THE K-I-T-E MONTH (March W-I-N-D)
APR	0	ON APRIL FOOLS' DAY I FOOLED NOBODY
MAY	2	"MAY DAY" IS TWO WORDS
JUN	5	THE B-R-I-D-E MONTH
JUL	0	ON JULY 4 I SHOT NO FIRECRACKERS
AUG	3	THE H-O-T MONTH
SEP	6	START OF A-U-T-U-M-N
OCT	1	A WITCH RIDES ONE BROOM
NOV	4	A C-O-O-L MONTH
DEC	6	BIRTH OF C-H-R-I-S-T

Keys and mnemonic aids for calendar trick

2. To the result of the preceding step add the month's key number. If possible, cast out 7's. March is **4 + r5 = 9** – 7 = **2.**

3. To the preceding result add the day of the month. Cast 7's if possible. The resulting digit gives the day of the week counting Saturday as 0, Sunday as 1, Monday as 2, and so on to Friday as 6. We use the previous total of 2 + (day) 23 = 25 – 21 (3 x 7) = 4. Now we count: 0 – Saturday, 1 – Sunday, etc. 4 is Wednesday, the birthday of the spectator in the crowd.

4. **Warning:** If the year is a leap year and the month is January or February, go back one day from the final result.

The first step automatically alerts you to leap years. Leap years are multiples of 4 and any number is a multiple of 4 if its last two digits are. Therefore if there is no remainder when you divide by 12, or none when you make the division by 4, you know it is a leap year.

(Bear in mind, however, that in the present Gregorian calendar system 1800 and 1900, although multiples of 4, are not leap years, whereas 2000 is. The reason is that the Gregorian calendar provides that a year ending in two zeros is a leap year only if it is evenly divisible by 400.)

The procedure just explained is restricted to dates in the 1900's, but only trivial final adjustments need to be made for dates in other centuries.

For the 1800's go two days forward in the week. For the 2000's go one day back. It is best not to allow dates earlier than the 1800's because of confusion involving the shift that took place in England and the American colonies on September 14, 1752, from the Julian to the Gregorian calendar. Julius Caesar had used a year of 365.25 days, with a day added in February every fourth year to compensate for that excess fraction of one-fourth. Unfortunately the year has 365.2422+ days, so with the passage of centuries the leap years overcompensated and a sizable error of excess days accumulated.

To prevent February from overtaking Easter (which depends on the vernal equinox), Pope Gregory XIII authorized the dropping of 10 days and the adoption of a calendar with fewer leap years. This was done throughout most of Europe in 1582, but in the English-speaking world the change was not made until 1752. The day after September 2 was called September 14, which explains why George Washington's birthday is now celebrated on February 22 instead of February 11, the actual date (Old Style) on which he was born. For dates in the 1700's, after the 1752 change-over, go forward four days in the week.

Another example will help make the procedure clearer.

Suppose this time you are informed that someone in the audience was born on July 28, 1929. What was the day of the week? Your mental calculations are as follows:

1. The **29** of 1929 contains two **(2)** 12's, with a remainder of **5.** Four goes into 5 (**1**). Then **2 + 5 + 1 = 8.** Casting out 7's reduces this to **1**.

2. The key for July is **0,** so nothing is added. The **1** is still kept in mind.

3. The day of the month, **28,** is added to **1**. Cast out **7's** from 29. The remainder is **1**. Your subject was born **on a Sunday**. Saturday is zero (0). In actual practice this last step can be simplified by recognizing **that 28 equals zero, modulo 7, so that there is nothing** to add to the previous 1.)

The fourth step is omitted because 1929 is not a leap year. Even if it were, the step would still be left out because the month is not January or February, the only months for which leap year adjustments must be made.

To review: 1929, (throw away the 19) -> 29 ÷ 12 = 2 (remainder of 5). 5 ÷ 4 = 1. So far 2 + 5 + 1 = 8 – throw away any 7. Remainder to here is 1. Month – July – 0. 28th day of July ÷ 7 = 0 (multiples of modulo 7.) So far all we've got is **1.** So **1 is Sunday.** We'll make you into a genius or strain our brains doing it.

From time to time so-called idiot savants get into the news by exhibiting an ability to perform this trick. A recent case of calendar-calculating twins with I.Q.'s in the 60-to-80 range was studied by psychiatrists and reported in *Scientific American* (August, 1965).

It seems unlikely that any mysterious ability is operating in these such cases. If the idiot savant takes a long time to give the day, he has probably memorized the first days of each year, over a wide range, and simply counting forward in his mind from those key days to the given date. If he then gives the day rapidly he has probably used a similar method to the one described here, or has come across it in a book or magazine.

Many methods for calculating the day of the week mentally were published late in the 19th century, but the author found none earlier than a method invented by Lewis Carroll and his explanation in *Nature* (Vol. 35, March 31, 1887, page 517). The method is essentially the same as one described here.

"I am not a rapid computer myself," Carroll wrote, "and as I find my average time for doing any such question is about 20 seconds, I have little doubt that a rapid computer would not need 15."

Further Thoughts

The trick of doing rapid multiplication by mentally dividing has endless variations. One of Griffiths "The Marvellous" famous tricks was to multiply a large number by 125. Because 1/8 = .125, you simply append three zeros and divide by 8. (See Short Cut No. 19.)

The number 1,443 can be quickly multiplied by a two-digit number, *ab,* by dividing *ababab* by 7, and 3,367 can be multiplied by *ab* by dividing *ababab* by 3. (Reason: 1,443 = 10101 ÷ 7 and 3,367 = 10101 ÷ 3.)

The non-stuttering magic number 1,667 was Martin Gardner's discovery, as well as 8,335. To multiply 8,335 by a three-digit number, *abc,* append a zero to *abc* and divide by 12. Halve the remainder, if any, carry it back to the beginning, and (keeping zero at the end) divide by 6. It works because half of 1,667 is 833.5. Martin said "I could think of no other four-digit numbers convenient to use in this manner. For a way of using the two numbers in a card trick, see my (Gardner's) 'Clairvoyant Multiplication' in the Indian magic periodical *Swami*, March, 1972, page 12."

Edgar A. Blair, Major W. H. Carter, and Kurt Eisemann each suggested a real way of remembering the key numbers for the months that is probably easier for mathemagicians than methods which employ key words. If grouped in triplets the keys are:

144 (Jan, Feb, Mar)
025 (Apr, May, Jun)
036 (Jul, Aug, Sep)
146 (Oct, Nov, Dec)

Note that the first three triplets are the squares of 12, 5, and 6, and that the last triplet, 146, is just 2 more than the first square.

We would like to bring to your attention the marvelous work done by the late Jakow Trachtenberg. His book on *Basic Arithmetic,* a high speed system not using a calculator, but just a basic brain is the most fascinating book I have ever read on the subject. The library Dewey is 513.92 Cutler. Get it as soon as possible.

PECULIAR ANSWERS

The MAGIC NUMBERS used in the lightning multiplication tricks operate on a principle best explained by examples. The number 142,857,143 is obtained by dividing 1,000,000,001 by 7. If 1,000,000,001 is multiplied by any nine-digit number, *abc,def,ghi,* the product obviously will be quite a large one: *abc,def, ghi,abc,def,ghi.*

Therefore in order to multiply 142,857,143 by *abc,def,ghi* we have only to divide *abc,def,ghi,abc,def,ghi* by 7.

The second magic number, 2,857,143, is equal to 20,000,001 divided by 7. It is easy to see that in this case why a 7-digit multiplier of 2,857,143 must be doubled before the first division by 7 is made. Insisting that each digit of the multiplier be greater than 4 (thus ensuring that there is always 1 to carry as each digit is doubled) makes possible the doubling procedure explained in the previous chapter. Without this proviso it is still possible to double and divide in the head, but the rules are more complicated.

The smaller magic numbers 143 and 1,667 operate in similar ways. The first is equal to 1,001 ÷ 7 and the second to 5,001 ÷ 3. In the second case the multiplier, *abc,* must be multiplied by 5 before the first division by 3 is made. Since multiplying by 5 is the same as multiplying by 10 and dividing by 2, we add a zero to *abc* and divide by 6 as explained in the last chapter. The remainder must be halved, to convert it from sixths to thirds, and brought to the front for the second division, which is by 3. The fact that the second division is by a different number prevents the quotient from stuttering, something that always occurs if 143 is used and the multiplier, *abc,* happens to be a multiple of 7.

TRIVIA TIME!

Is there an easy way to add large columns of numbers?

$$\begin{array}{r} 1\,2\,3 \\ 6\,5\,4 \\ \underline{9\,8\,7} \\ 17\,6\,4 \end{array}$$

This is an easy and rapid way to add three columns of figures at the same time. Merely take the top number (123) and add the units figure of the next lower number (4) to get 12?. Then add the tens figure (5, which is really 50) to 127, giving 177. Next add the hundreds figure (6, or really 600) to 177, which yields 777. Then add the figure in the units column of the bottom row (7) to get 784; the tens figure (8) to get 864; and the hundreds figure (9) to get 1,764. Once you have learned this trick, you can run down such a column of figures, noting the successive sums as you go: 123, 127, 177, 777, 784, 864, and 1,764. Of course, you can run up as well as down just as readily and the sum will be just as correct.

Adding Tricks!

Writing down such a sum with little apparent effort never ceases to amaze the uninitiated. You can use a bit of trickery, however, to produce an even greater effect. Ask a friend to write a number having about five or six digits and then you write a similar number directly underneath it. Be sure, however, that your number and his are related as follows:

495,378 (your friend's number
504,622 (your number)

Starting with the left-hand side (to look casual) select each digit so that when added to the one above, the sum is 9. Do this until you reach the last digit and select this one to yield 10. (As you can see, this process gives 1,000,000). Then have your friend write another number and follow the same technique with your number. Repeat this process several times and when your last turn comes up, write down any figures at all so long as the sums are less than 9.

```
  495,378
  504,622
  473,291
  526,709
  974,531
   25,469
  425,823
  123,022
3,548,845
```

To add the column start at the left, put down a 3, (there are 3 pairs of 1,000,000's above). Then add the last 2 rows, placing the figures in their proper order. This trick goes over very well. *Don't repeat it too often.!!*

I WOULD SAY THE CUBE OF YOUR DIMENSIONS WOULD BE A LOVELY 46656, 10648, 46656!
SMART CAT

Chapter 18

CUBES and CUBE ROOTS

Number	Cubes
1	1
2	8
3	27
4	64
5	125
6	216
7	343
8	512
9	729
10	1000

The first thing about this table is that the numbers from 0 to 9 all occur. If a number is cubed one can therefore determine the units figure of the cube root immediately. If a cubed number ends in 1, 4, 5, 6, 9, or 0, its cube root will end in the same number. If it ends in 2, the cube root will end in 8; and if it ends in 8, the cube root will and in 2. Similarly if the number ends in 7 the units digit of the cube root will be 3, and if it ends in 3 the units digit of the cube root will be 7. So you see that 7 and 3, 8 and 2 add up to 10. Keep that in mind. You will also need this table when you come to determine the tens digit.

If a cube has four, five, or six digits the root will contain two. To extract the root first divide the number into two groups by counting left three places from the units digit. For instance if you are extracting the cube root of 195112 divide it as follows:

195 112

Find the first digit of the cube root by looking back mentally to the table of cubes. 195 falls between 125 and 216 – between 5^3 and 6^3: the tens figure of the cube root you are looking for will be the root of the lower number – in this instance the 2. Now, find the units digit, again you know from the table on the previous page that if the cubed number ends in a 2, its tens complement is 8. If you can't understand this move, then read it over again. Everything is hard the first time. If you've ever ridden a bike, you'll understand.

The cube root you are looking for is 58.

To find the cube root of 97,336, divide the number into groups:

97 336

97 falls in between the cubes of 4 and 5. The tens unit is therefore 4. The whole number ends in 6, the cube root therefore ends in 6. The cube root is 46.

To extract the cube root of larger numbers – having some seven, eight or nine digits – is as easy if you have learned still another table:

X	Y
1	1
2	7
3	9
4	5
5	3
6	8
7	6
8	2
9	4
10	10

We seriously encourage the reader to practice using this table. It is important to memorize the rhythm of 17953 – 8624-10.

Refer to your fingers in order to lock in on the right value of Y. X is the value that leads to the final charm of this trick. So do your homework before you try this on stage. **It's a winner!**

If you are given a number with seven, eight, or nine digits, you will have a cube root with three digits. To get the root we begin by dividing the number into groups of three, moving from right to left. For instance, compute the cube root below. But first, let's divide it in the following manner:

155 720 872

To find the hundreds unit of the cube root think back to the table of cubes from 1 to 10 on page 121. 155 falls between the cubes of 5 and 6, so 5 is the hundreds unit of the root we are extracting. The units digit – the terminal figure of the cube root – must, we already know, be 8, for the last digit of the cubed number is 2. (8 x 8 x 8 = 51**2.** Remember, 1, 4, 5, 6, and 9, are always the same digit when cubed. Digits 2, and 8, as well as 3, and 7, are paired as complements of 10.

Now Comes Your Brain Power!

Now then, we have to find the tens digit. This calls for a special technique used by stage calculators for as far back as the mid-1800s. First add up the odd digits of the original number – the first, third, fifth, seventh, and ninth figures in the number, reading from right to left. Subtract from this odd sum number the sum of the even figures in the number (the second, fourth, sixth, and eighth digits) added up in the same way. **IMPORTANT**: If the total of the even figures is greater than that of the odd figures **add 11** to the latter before subtracting.

Let us now get to that middle missing number:

2 + 8 + 2 + 5 + 1 = 18

(the sum of the odd digits) from which we subtract

7 + 0 + 7 + 5 = 19

(the sum of the even digits) to get a remainder of – 1.

18 + 11 = 29. Or 19 + 10 = 29. At this point we must add 11 to –1, giving a remainder of 10. We now refer back to the table with columns X and Y.

Find in the X column the number just obtained as a remainder and note the number opposite it in the Y column. Add together the two digits of the final root which you have already (that is, the hundreds and the units digits, respectively

In the example the remainder was 10, this stands opposite 10 in the table, so we subtract that figure from the sum of 5 and 8

$$5 + 8 = 13 \qquad 13 - 10 = \mathbf{3}$$

which gives us the tens unit of the cube root. The complete root is **538**.

If the sum of the hundreds and units digits is less than that obtained from column Y of the table add 11 to that sum before making the subtraction. Here is yet another example.

Find the cube root of 99,252,847.

Divide the number into groups:

99 252 847

The hundreds digit of the root is 4 as 99 stands between the cubes of 4 and 5 (64 and 125).

The units digit is 3 as the number ends in 7. Remember 3 –> 7 = 10, or 7 –> 3 = 10.

The sum of the digits in the odd places is

$$7 + 8 + 5 + 9 = \underline{\mathbf{29}}$$

from which is subtracted the sum of the even digits.

$$\mathbf{29} - (4 + 2 + 2 + 9 = 17) - \mathbf{17} = \mathbf{12}$$

In the table, 12 in the X column stands opposite 1 in the Y column (since anything over 11 automatically is decreased by that 11, therefore 12 – 11 = 1. For 1 in X column read 1 in the

Y column The sum of the digits, (hundreds digit and units digit) already arrived at (4 + 3 = 7), minus the digit from the Y column, gives the tens unit of the cube root (7 – 1 = 6). The cube root is then 463.

Before we leave cube rooting. Note that if odd number minus even number is 0, that zero is equivalent to 11.

LET'S EXTRACT SOME FIFTH ROOTS

With a number raised to the fifth power, the root is so easy to find. If the number has between six to ten digits in it the root will have but two digits.

The units digit of all fifth roots is the same as the units digit of the fifth power number, so all you have to do is locate the tens digit. Do this by dividing the number at the fifth place, reading from right to left. For instance, if the number of which you are trying to find the fifth root is 1453933568 divide it as follows:

14539 33568

For the next step you need patience again. There's a table to memorize – that of fifth powers of numbers from I to 10:

Number	**Fifth Power**
1	1
2	32
3	243
4	1024
5	3125
6	7776
7	16807
8	32768
9	59049
10	100000

When you have committed the above table to memory, (you should carry around a copy of these different tables and review them until you know them better than your own middle name).

You can speedily know where the left-hand fifth power group fits into the table: 14539 slides in between 6^5 and 7^5, then the fifth root of 1453933568 is 68. Always go for the lower of the pair of powers that lie on each side of the number for which you are searching.

Care for another one: Try to find the fifth power of 550731776:

First divide as suggested: 5507 31776

5507 comes between the fifth powers of 5 and 6 in the table, the fifth root is therefore 5 followed by the final digit of the original number: 56.

By using similar methods other roots can be found. Seventh, ninth, thirteenth, seventeenth, twenty-first roots are like fifth roots in that the power and the root have the same terminal digit – you can extract the root by working out and memorizing tables of powers from 1 to 10.

Other roots – fourth, sixth, eighth, and so on, can be extracted by the same methods as those described here for square, cube, and fifth roots. Try working some of these out for yourself. You will be a master calculator if you get the hang of it!

Here's a Teaser! But It's a Week One!

"How old are you, Bob?" Bob answered, "26 years old, Jim. Why?"

"Well," continued Bob, "not only are you 26 years old, but you're also 1,352 weeks old!"

"C'mon, Bob, how did you reckon that so fast?" Silence from Bob. Jim was puzzled for several days. Then he read SUPER MATH-E-MAGICS for the first time, and there was the answer.

(This book has the foundations for stage calculators!)

Here's how it works:

Divide the years by 2 – this gives the 1st two digits (26 ÷ 2 = 13), then multiply the years by 2 – giving 2nd two digits (26 x 2 = 52).

(P.S. from Bob) "If you're age is less than 20 years, then division only gives one digit. Say you are 12 years old, the number of weeks will be about (12 ÷ 2 = 6) (12 x 2 = 24).Answer is 624 weeks. Another example: 16 ÷ 2 = 8; 16 x 2 = 32. Answer: 832 weeks.

" Sure, Bob, but what about having an odd years old? Let's say, 15 years old, maybe."

"Well – take the half of 15, that is, 7.5, and add it to the tens digit in the multiplication; e.g.: 15 ÷ 2 = 7.50 (only read the 7), then 15 x 2 = 30; 50 + 30 = 80. Therefore you're 780 weeks old."

(To do fast reckoning, HINT: Short Cut 5 – To multiply by 50, add 2 zeros and divide by 2; or, multiply by 100 and divide by 2.)

Did you ever have to square a number made up of just 9's?

Put down from left to right as many 9's less one as the number you have to square, place one 8, and as many zeros as there are nines in the answer and tack on the digit 1.

Example:

$$9^2 = 81$$
$$99^2 = 9801$$
$$999^2 = 998001$$
$$9,999^2 = 99980001$$
$$99,999^2 = 9999800001$$

and so on. (notice 4 nines and 4 zeros!

Exercise 14 – See Pages 23.3 through 23.7

(Multiply these numbers the Trachtenberg Method)

1. 56171 x 304	5. 678196 x 829	9. 34696 x 367
2. 981357 x 4294	6. 381358 x 67	10. 44369 x 85834
3. 834 x 27	7. 15355 x 299	11. 37269 x 612
4. 477 x 312	8. 64840 x 350	12. 6578 x 6578

I ASKED HIM IF HE WANTED A DATE SQUARE ... SOMETIMES I JUST BREAK MYSELF UP!
a^2

Chapter 19

DATE SQUARES ANYONE?

Now that I have your attention!

The square of a number is the number multiplied by itself. Squares may be determined quickly if the given number is considered to be the sum of two numbers. In algebra such a sum would ordinarily be taken as $a + b$ and its square would be $a^2 + 2\,ab + b^2$. In regular arithmetical cases a becomes the tens of the number and b the units. Therefore, 26 is 20 + 6, and 158 is 150 + 8. The algebraic formula for the square of the sum of two numbers is expressed as the square of the first plus twice the product of the first by the second plus the square of the second. Ergo, 26 squared is 20 x 20 (400) plus 2 x 20 x 6 (240) plus 6 x 6 (36); the total is 676.

In computing squares by this principle you may immediately join the square of the second to the square of the first and then add twice the product of the first by the second. Then in squaring 26 you would immediately think 436, and then add to this 2 x 20 x 6 (240), making 676. In squaring 158 you immediately say 22564 and add to this 2 x 150 x 8 (2400), making 24964. Always allow two places for the square of the second. In squaring 71 the first partial product is 4901, to which 140 is added to make 5041.

As a precaution when squaring numbers on paper, it would be wise to set the number twice as it were to be done in the old manner. Multiply units by units and tens by tens, mentally. Write the units down and continue to the tens portion. Again doing it without any carrying being jotted down. Remember, add the two given tens together, multiply this sum by the given units, add the carried figure, write tens in the result and carry hundreds. Multiply tens by tens, add the carried figure and write the answer.

Example:

67	136	2714
67	136	2714
4489	18496	7365796

In the first example on the left, 7 x 7 = 49, write down **9,** and carry 4; 6 + 6 = 12, 12 x 7 = 84, 84 + 4 = 88; write **8** and carry 8; 6 x 6 = 36, 36 + 8 = **44**. Write 44. Answer is therefore 4489.

Let's try the 136 x 136, the middle one this time. 6 x 6 = 36, write **6** and carry 3; 13 + 13 = 26, 26 x 6 = 156, 156 + 3 = 159, write **9** and carry 15; 13 x 13 = 169, 169 + 15 = 184, write **184**. Full answer – 18496.

The third example is slightly different. because some of the parts are 27 and 14 (27 as in 2700, and 14 as a full tens and units number).

14 x 14 = 196, write **96** two figures!), carrying **1**; 27 + 27 = 54, 54 x 14 = 702, (50 x 14 = 1400 ÷ 2 = 700, 4 x 14 = 56 + 700 = 756 – remember the rules for large numbers), 756 + 1 = 757, write **57** and carry **7**; 27 x 27 = (Remember Boomerang, Stage 2 – (27 + 7 = 34(0) x 2 = 680 + (7 x 7 = 49) = 729, + 7 carry over = 736. write down **736**. Altogether, answer is 7365796 or 7,365,796. (even much neater)

Square some of the following as per first and second methods:

A.	1. 74	4. 64	7. 124	10. 186	13. 1523
	2. 93	5. 38	8. 146	11. 1217	14. 1826
	3. 82	6. 112	9. 168	12. 1568	15. 1919

Multiplying Three Figures by Three

Exercise B: Multiply mentally the following combinations:

1. 161 x 205	4. 136 x 56	7. 195 x 115
2. 159 x 379	5. 234 x 174	8. 885 x 899
3. 172 x 492	6. 217 x 197	9. 567 x 765

Exercise 15
Mentally Multiply Four Figures by Four

1. 4592 x 6973
2. 5623 x 4973
3. 6675 x 9829
4. 2684 x 7844
5. 3576 x 5849
6. 8647 x 6959
7. 6788 x 9767
8. 2869 x 4563

Exercise 16
Go to Table 4 – Page 13.5

Add Columns A and B, add both totals and square. Add C and D, do same. Multiply both answers. What answer did you get? Do the same with Columns E, F and G, H. Check answers.

What are logarithms?

(See 16.12 for remarks on Logarithms)

Suppose you were asked to choose between adding two 19-digit numbers or to multiply them; what would elect to do? More likely you would opt for the adding. Addition is simpler than multiplication – especially if it gives large answers. So math types long ago set their minds to a new routine – **Logarithms.**

So a great reduction in effort was effected in the multiplication of large numbers in contrast to the time-study of addition. Logarithms were invented to do just that thing. We will illustrate the fundamental principle involved. Let's write a couplet of numbers, one above the other.

1	2	3	4	5	6	7	8	9
3^1	3^2	3^3	3^4	3^5	3^6	3^3	3^8	3^9
3	9	27	81	243	729	2,187	6,561	19,683

The lowest series of numbers given above is equal to, of course, the second. The principle, known to Archimedes, was and still is this: pick two numbers in the bottom series which you want multiplied: 81 and 243. Add the corresponding numbers in the top series, 4 + 5 = 9. Go to column 8 and read the answer as 19,683. As you can see,

$$3^4 + 3^5 = 3^{4+5} = 3^9$$

or, in general terms,

$$a^m + a^n = a^{m+n}$$

where a is any base number, and m and n are any exponents. This principle tells us that we can convert multiplication into addition if we change the form of the numbers to be multiplied from M and N, to a^m and a^n, and if we happen to have a suitable table of numbers. If M and N are any two numbers to be multiplied we must set

$$M = a^m$$
$$N = a^n$$

For the sake of convenience, we can assume $a = 10$, since most logarithm tables are made up on this basis. Then

$$M = 10^m$$
$$N = 10^n$$

We can now define a logarithm in the following way:

$$\log_{10} M = m$$
$$\log_{10} N = n$$

The operator $\log_{10}$ should be treated as a mathematical noun which means **the logarithm**, to the *base* 10, of. Many textbooks omit the subscript 10 since the logarithm is understood to be of base 10 unless otherwise indicated. Similarly, an "antilogarithm" is just the reverse of a log.

$$\text{antilog}_{10}\, n = N$$

In order to multiply M by N using logs, we must perform the operations indicated in the following equation:

$$M \times N = \text{antilog}\,(\log \mathbf{M} + \log N)$$

This equation asks us to look up log M and log N in a table of logarithms, add these two numbers together, and find the antilogarithm of the sum by reversing the way we use the tables.

In practice, there are some complications involved in the use of logarithm tables which ought to be discussed before leaving the subject. First of all, a logarithm usually consists of a number having a whole number portion followed by a decimal fraction. The logarithm of 280, for example, is 2.4472. The logarithmic tables, however, will give you only 4472.

You must get the 2 on your own initiative. The 2 in this case is called the characteristic of the logarithm, and the .4472 is called the mantissa In order to determine the characteristic, merely count the number of digits to the left of the decimal point in the number, and subtract 1 from that amount The number 280 has three such digits, so the characteristic of its logarithm is 2.

To illustrate the use of logarithms, let's multiply 280 x 43.

$$\log 280 = 2.4472$$

$$\log 43 = \underline{1.6335}$$
$$\log 280 + \log 43 = 4.0807$$

$$\text{antilog } 4.0807 = 12{,}040 = 280 \times 43$$

The first table of logarithms was compiled by Briggs in the 1631 edition of *Logarithmall Arithmetike*. Briggs couldn't keep himself from pressing their value ". . . by them all troublesome multiplications and divisions are avoided and performed only by addition instead of multiplication and subtraction instead of division." The world as come a long way since 1631, however, and today even the use of logarithms is being superseded by mechanical and electronic machines. These machines can not only multiply and divide, but they can solve difficult equations and guide a missile around the moon. Technological progress, it seems, will eventually give to logarithms a place beside the abacus in mathematical oblivion.

Have you thought of entering in the International Students" Math Contest? See your Math Teacher or Professor, times and dates are available. Let your tests show just where you stand on the ladder of knowledge and intelligence. Maybe you're that untested genius for whom we're all waiting!

Here's a Quick Counter for your Calculations!

	1	**2**	**3**	**4**	**5**	**6**	**7**	**8**	**9**	**10**	**11**	**12**	**13**	**14**	**15**
1	1	2	3	4	5	6	7	8	9	10	11	12	13	14	15
2	2	4	6	8	10	12	14	16	18	20	22	24	26	28	30
3	3	6	9	12	15	18	21	24	27	30	33	36	39	42	45
4	4	8	12	16	20	24	28	32	36	40	44	48	52	56	60
5	5	10	15	20	25	30	35	40	45	50	55	60	65	70	75
6	6	12	18	24	30	36	42	48	54	60	66	72	78	84	90
7	7	14	21	28	35	42	49	56	63	70	77	84	91	98	105
8	8	16	24	32	40	48	56	64	72	80	88	96	104	112	120
9	9	18	27	36	45	54	63	72	81	90	99	108	117	126	135
10	10	20	30	40	50	60	70	80	90	100	110	120	130	140	150
11	11	22	33	44	55	66	77	88	99	110	121	132	143	154	165
12	12	24	36	48	60	72	84	96	108	120	132	144	156	168	180
13	13	26	39	52	65	78	91	104	117	130	143	156	169	182	195
14	14	28	42	56	70	84	98	112	126	140	154	168	182	196	210
15	15	30	45	60	75	90	105	120	135	150	165	180	195	210	225

OK! So I Promised You Date Squares!

Some call these Matrimonial Cakes in Western Canada. These squares are very scrumptious. Try to use freshly pitted dates.

Date Filling:

2 cups	packed chopped pitted dates (2/3-lb. – 350g)	500 mL
1 cup	cold coffee	250 mL
2 tbsp	brown sugar	25 mL
	Grated rind and juice of half an orange	
1 tbsp	lemon juice	15 mL

Crumb Mixture:

1-1/4 cups	all-purpose flour	300 mL
1 tsp	baking powder	5 mL
1/2 tsp	baking soda	2 mL
1/2 tsp	salt	2 mL
3/4 cup	butter	175 mL
1-1/4 cups	rolled oats	300 mL
3/4 cup	lightly packed brown sugar	175 mL

Date Filling: In small saucepan, combine dates, coffee, brown sugar and orange rind; bring to a boil. Reduce heat and simmer, uncovered, until mixture is soft enough to mash and has the consistency of jam (runny but easy to spread), about 10 minutes. Remove from heat; stir in orange and lemon juices. Let cool.

Crumb Mixture: Sift together flour, baking powder, baking soda and salt. With pastry blender or 2 knives, cut in butter until mixture is the size of small peas. Stir in rolled oats and sugar. Press half of the crumb mixture firmly into 9-inch/2 L square baking pan. Spread date mixture evenly over crumb mixture and top with remaining crumbs, pressing lightly. Bake in 325°F/160°C oven for 25 minutes or until lightly browned. Makes about 24/25 squares.

Calories per square: 150;
Grams fat per square: 6;
Three squares are an excellent source of fiber.

(P.S.: Good Food For Thought!)

NOW... LETS
DISCUSS PI
π

Chapter 20

π

and Some Tricky Short Cuts

π . . . pi – the Greek letter, stands for peripheral – meaning circumference. The Babylonians, around 2200 B.C., were most taken with squaring the circle. The closest they came to a useable figure (25/8) was a ratio of a circle's circumference to the diameter. Q. Who gave the name "Pi" to this magic number?

π = 3.14159265355897932384626433832795028841971693993 105875105820974944559207816 4 . . . etc., going on endlessly to astronomical and impossible limits (totology?), presently passing the four billion mark. When Archimedes tried to compute π he found it to be between 3-1/7 and 3-10/71.

The Bible, Book of Kings 1, vii-23, *"And he made a molten sea, 10 cubits from the one brim to the other; it was round all about, and its height was five cubits; and a line of 30 cubits did compass it round about. . . .",* placed it as 3.

The pharoah's scientists(?) or mathematicians clearly favored (257/82) 3.16, and Ptolemy, circa 150 a.d., said it was 3.1416. Pi – π – is an irrational number. Adrien-Marie Legendre believed, and Ferdinand Lindemann proved, that π was a "transcendental number", that is, being a number that "transcends algebra". Meaning that it is not the solution of any algebraic equation. So let's just treat it as a constant in any of our calculations. The most important formula is the area of a circle equals π times the square of the circle's radius ($A = \pi R^2$).

Have you found an easy method to remember the value of π?

There's one good method that I know of that will come in handy in the classroom. A mnemonic sentence that gives the sequence of letters by the count of the value if Pi. Instead of guessing what number comes after "3.141592, uh, hmm, duh!", keep a familiar, a quotation, perhaps, up your mental sleeve. For instance, try this one. Some 90 years ago, an American printed a rhyming phrase or sentence:

"Now I – even I, could celebrate,	3.14159
In Rhymes inept,the great	26535
Immortal Assyrians rivaled never more,	89754
Who in his wondrous lore	32384
Moved on before,	526
Gave men his guidance	4338
How to circles calculate.	3279

Here you have Pi to approximately 30 places.
So much for Pi, you've had a taste of dessert. Let's go forward.

The following is a variation of my favorite Short Cut.

Multiplying Units Digits That Are Alike

This method is a variation of multiplying numbers that contain small squares in their make-up.

$$\begin{array}{r} 67 \\ \underline{87} \\ 5829 \end{array} \qquad \begin{array}{r} 414 \\ \underline{914} \\ 378396 \end{array}$$

In the above example at the left, 7 x 7 = 49, write 9 and carry 4; 8 + 6 = 14, 14 x 7 = 98, 98 + 4 = 102, write **2,** and carry 10; 6 x 8 = 48, 48 + 10 = 58. Write down **58,** then whole answer appears –> **5829.**

The right-hand problem is similar to the square of 414, so let's demonstrate how this one works:
14 x 14 = 196, write **96** and carry 1; 9 + 4 = 13, 13 x 14 = (two ways here, you either know by rote the 13 times table, which is

182, or the Boomerang method, 14 + 3 (of 14) 170 + (3 x 4 =) 12, equals 182), so 13 x 14 = 182, 182 + 1 = 183, write **83,** carry 1; 4 x 9 = 36 +1 = **37**. Then the answer is: **378396.**
Easier using the Lenaghan Squaring Way? (see page 16.11)

Exercise D: Do the following by the above methods.

1. 334 x 64	4. 395 x 165	7. 1516 x 1316
2. 159 x 99	5. 278 x 178	8. 712 x 912
3. 72 x 72	6. 207 x 297	9. 837 x 637

If you have been jumping about turning pages for some odd things to do – look at Chapter 23. The Trachtenberg Method of Speedy Arithmetic will amaze you. Before you say, "Yah! No way!" try it, you'll like it!.

Try squaring these numbers the Two Finger Method. You're in for a shock. You'll never get another chance like this technique. It's powerful, downright simple, and it'll make you a genius!

Cubes of Numbers

The algebraic formula for the cube of the sum of two numbers, a and b, is $a^3 + 3a^2b + 3ab^2 + b^3$. This may be expressed as the cube of the first plus three times the square of the first multiplied by the second, plus three times the first multiplied by the square of the second plus the cube of the second.
By applying this formula it is not very difficult to calculate mentally the cubes of numbers of two places. Suppose, for instance, that we want to find the cube of 36. We immediately annex the cube of 6 (216) to the cube of 3 (27), 27216. (Always allow three places for the cube of the second.) Multiplying 3 x 900 (square of 30) x 6, we get 16200, which, added to 27216, makes 43416. Multiplying 3 x 30 x 36 (square of 6) we obtain 3240, which added to 43416 gives 46656 as the cube of 36.

Cubes may be written down from right to left by using an entirely different method.

36^3	6 x 6 x 6 = 216	6
46656	(6 x 6 x 3 x 3) 324 + 21 = 345	5
	(6 x 3 x 3 x 3) 162 + 34 = 196	6
	(3 x 3 x 3) 27 + 19 = 46	46

Let's analyze the calculations we just made. The cube of 6 is 216, write 6 and carry 21. The square of 6 (36) multiplied by 3 (108) multiplied by 3 (324) + 21 = 345, write down 5, and carry 34. The product of 6 times the square of 3 (9) multiplied by 3. 6(27) + 34 = 196, write 6 and carry 19. Lastly, the cube of 3 is 27, when added to the carry of 19, equals 46. Therefore, the answer appear as 46656.

Please learn all the cubes 2 through 20 for openers, and continuing on to at least 30. It may seem tough at first, but you'll whiz through the list after a few weeks of exposure.

It is an important ritual that will perfect, first, your retentivity, (sure it is a rote method), but your mom made you repeat over and over, your name, address and phone number, or lose you.

Secondly, to have the power, the grasp, the amazement of your peers, that you are a master calculator, makes others respect you for your mental capability. Thirdly, and most important, you are confident, self-reliant, and above all else, your a brainy person. Your whole demeanor, walk, poise will radiate to those about you. "He's a mathematician!" Happy feeling, isn't it!"

Talking about Calendars . . . Well, I thought I was! But now that I've mentioned it . . .

This Calendar Ploy works like a charm. It's Called Date Magic. Offer the audience a sheet from a calendar, any sheet, or month, that is.

You ask a spectator to mark off a day in each week. Having done that to his satisfaction, and always keeping your back to the audience as well, ask him/her, "How many Sundays are ticked off?" "How many Mondays?, Tuesdays? Wednesdays?, etc. Quickly after this information is obtained, you give his answer. Your spectator is asked to add up the dates marked. The addition correctly matches your earlier number.

S	M	T	W	T	F	S
			1	2	3	4
5	6	7	8	9	10	11
12	13	14	15	16	17	18
19	20	21	22	23	24	25
26	27	28	29	30	31	

How it works:

The calendar page is shown below. Make sure that there are 5 Wednesdays in the months you choose. You must have already figured the total calendar days ahead, **in this case the Wednesday column adds up to 75.** This is important for the trick. As long as there only one check in each line, the guest may check the same day, in another week. Remember this: Wednesday = 0; Sunday = minus 3; Mon. = – 2; Tues. = – ; Wed. = 0; Thurs. = +1; Fri. = +2; Sat. = +3.

When asked how many Sundays, the answer is 1. That's – 3. One Mon. = –2 (so far, –5. One Tues. = –1. (–6). One Wed. = 0, holding at – 6. One Thur. = +1 (holding – 5). If key calendar Wednesday column totals 75, then the – 5 makes the total struck out as 70. Make the quick calculation and take a bow.

Exercise 17

Cube the following list of numbers.

12	6	4	8	11	3	9	5
2	13	14	7	10	–1	16	20

Exercise 18

Square These Figures – The Stage Calculator Method
(See Page **16**.11 – Mentally)

1. 452	4. 65782	7. 988	10. 1849	13. 6162
2. 7074	5. 747	8. 166	11. 418	14. 67853
3. 674	6. 294	9. 289	12. 668	15. 999

Now here's a Think for the day!

We think so because other people
all think so;
Or because – or because – after all,
we do think so;
Or because we were told so,
and think we must think so;
Or because we once thought so,
and think we still think so;
Or because, having thought so,
we think we will think so.

HENRY SIDGEWICK – Lines which came to him in his sleep.

CUBES

1.	1	26.	17,576	51.	132,651	76.	438,976
2.	8	27.	19,683	52.	140,608	77.	456,533
3.	27	28.	21,952	53.	148,877	78.	474,552
4.	64	29.	24,389	54.	157,464	79.	493,039
5.	125	30.	27,000	55.	166,375	80.	512,000
6.	216	31.	29,791	56.	175,616	81.	531,441
7.	343	32.	32,768	57.	185,193	82.	551,368
8.	512	33.	35,937	58.	195,112	83.	571,787
9.	729	34.	39,304	59.	205,379	84.	592,704
10.	1,000	35.	42,875	60.	216,000	85.	614,125
11.	1,331	36.	42,656	61.	226,981	86.	636,056
12.	1,728	37.	50,653	62.	238,328	87.	658,503
13.	2,197	38.	54,872	63.	250,047	88.	681,472
14.	2,744	39.	59,319	64.	262,114	89.	704,969
15.	3,375	40	64,000	65.	274,625	90.	729,000
16.	4,096	41.	68,921	66.	287,496	91.	753,571
17.	4,913	42.	74,088	67.	300,763	92.	778,688
18.	5,832	43.	79,507	68.	314,432	93.	804,357
19.	6,859	44.	85,184	69.	328,509	94.	830,584
20.	8,000	45.	91,125	70.	343,000	95.	857,375
21.	9,261	46.	97,336	71.	357,911	96.	884,736
22.	10,648	47.	103,823	72.	373,248	97.	912,673
23.	12,167	48.	110,592	73.	389,017	98.	941,192
24.	13,824	49.	117,649	74.	405,224	99.	970,299
25.	15,625	50.	125,000	75.	421,875	100.	1,000,000

SQUARES AND SQUARES ROOTS OF NUMBERS

n	n^2	$\sqrt{n}$	n	n^2	$\sqrt{n}$
1	1	1.000	30	900	5.477
2	4	1.414	31	961	5.568
3	9	1.732	32	1024	5.657
4	16	2.000	33	1089	5.745
5	25	2.236	34	1156	5.831
6	36	2,449	35	1225	5.916
7	49	2.646	36	1296	6.000
8	64	2.828	37	1369	6.083
9	81	3.000	38	1444	6.164
10	100	3.162	39	1521	6.245
11	121	3.317	40	1600	6.325

n	n^2	$\sqrt{n}$	n	n^2	$\sqrt{n}$
12	144	3.464	41	1681	6.403
13	169	3.606	42	1764	6.481
14	196	3.742	43	1849	6.557
15	225	3.873	44	1936	6.633
16	256	4.000	45	2025	6.708
17	289	4.123	46	2116	6.782
18	324	4.243	47	2209	6.856
19	361	4.359	48	2304	6.928
20	400	4.472	49	2401	7.000
21	441	4.583	50	2500	7.071
22	484	4.699	51	2601	7.141
23	529	4.796	52	2704	7.211
24	576	4.899	53	2809	7.280
25	625	5.000	54	2916	7.348
26	676	5.099	55	3025	7.416
27	729	5.196	56	3136	7.483
28	784	5.292	57	3249	7.550
29	841	5.385	58	3364	7.616

Review these squares until you know them like your middle name.

n	n^2	$\sqrt{n}$	n	n^2	$\sqrt{n}$
59	3481	7.681	80	6400	7.944
60	3600	7.746	81	6561	9.000
61	3721	7.810	82	6724	9.055
63	3969	7.937	83	6889	9.110
64	4096	8.000	84	7056	9.165
65	4225	8.062	86	7396	9.274
66	4356	8.124	87	7569	9.327
67	4489	8.185	88	7744	9.381
68	4624	8.246	89	7921	9.434
69	4761	8.307	90	8100	9.487
70	4900	8.367	91	8281	9.539
71	5041	8.426	92	8464	9.592
72	5184	8.485	93	8649	9.644
73	5329	8.544	94	8836	9.695
74	5476	8.602	95	9025	9.747
75	5625	8.660	96	9216	9.798
76	5776	8.718	97	9409	9.849
77	5929	8.775	98	9604	9.899
78	6084	8.832	99	9801	9.950
79	6241	8.888	100	10,000	10.000

We wish you a clear mind, healthy body, and a goal:

"Success in your Life, and above all else:
Keep your fists in your pockets and your big mouth shut!"

Anon.

WHAT ARE YOU... A WISEGUY? I SAID SHOW ME A COUPLE OF SHORT CUTS...NOT SHORT CATS!

Chapter 21

"A COUPLE OF SHORT CUTS TO GOOD NUMBER SENSE!"

FUNDAMENTALS OF SHORT-CUT METHODS

1.1 – Basic Ways of Simplifying Calculations

Short-cut methods are based upon the principle of changing "difficult" numbers and processes into easier ones. For example, to find the sum of 29 and 36, you can add 1 to 29 and subtract 1 from 36 so that the problem becomes 30 + 35; you can see at once that the answer is 65. Adding and subtracting 1 simplified the problem, but did not change the answer. This principle of 'equivalency' as used in short-cuts enables you to reach the right answer faster and easier.

You can apply the same principle to multiplying. Take 28 x 15, for instance. If you halve 28 (= 14), double 15 (= 30), you change these problem to 14 x 30, which, as you can see, is an easy 420 – the same answer you get by multiplying 28 by 15.

It's not always the size of a number that makes it difficult to handle but the *kind* of number it is. You know, of course, that it's much easier to multiply by 10 than by 9, even though 10 is the larger number. However, the "difficult" number 9 can be changed into two "easy" numbers, 10 minus 1, which equal 9. Therefore, to multiply a number by 9, you can multiply by 10 (simply add a zero to the number) and subtract the number, thus: 37 x 9 = 370 – 37 = 333. The 370 – 37 is, of course, 37 x (10 –1) instead of 37 x 9. Either way, the answer is the same.

Incidentally, the easiest numbers to handle are 0, 1, 10, and 20, although 100, 1,000, etc., are also easy to get along with; so are other "zero numbers," such as 20, 30, etc. If you can change a difficult number to one of these, you are on your way to an easier solution.

In many instances, you can do it faster and better and easier combining two or three simple calculations than trying to come to the answer in one motion. Taking long strides only gives you sore muscles. Don't poop out your brain. I'd rather have you do a hop-skip-and-a-jump than have you do it in one big leap. To multiply 64 by 25, for instance, you can divide 64 by 4 (= 16) and multiply by 100 (just add two zeros), and there's your answer: 1,600. This works because dividing by 4 and multiplying by 100 is the same as multiplying by 100/4 which equals 25. Again, the method has been greatly simplified but the answer is not changed because 25 and 100 ÷ 4 are the same.

Another basic way of simplifying a calculation is to break up the numbers into easier parts. For example, to divide by 16, you can divide first by 2 and then by 8, or divide twice by 4, since 2 x 8 and 4 x 4 are each equivalent to 16. Try dividing 16 into a number like 224. Divide the number in half (= 112) and divide this by 8 (= 14), or you can divide 224 by 4 (= 56) and divide again by 4 (= 14). Dividing 224 by 16 will, of course, give the same answer, 14, because all three ways of dividing are equivalent.

A number may be broken up into other parts, too, such as into units, tens, hundreds, etc. These smaller parts can make the number much easier to handle. The number 613, for instance, can be broken up into 600 + 10 + 3. If you want to multiply 613 by another number, such as by 12, you can multiply each part and then add the partial results to get the answer, such as:

$$\begin{array}{rcl} 600 \times 12 &=& 7,200 \\ 10 \times 12 &=& 120 \\ \underline{3} \times 12 &=& \underline{36} \\ 613 \times 12 &=& 7,356 \end{array}$$

Besides such methods as the foregoing, short-cuts are also based upon eliminating or easing processes that most people find difficult, such as "carrying" in addition and multiplication, "borrowing" in subtraction, the intricacies of "long" division, and the need to remember results when doing problems mentally.

1-2. Results Are What You Want

In doing a problem, it's better to think only of the results of each step and to omit any unnecessary details of the step itself. For example, when you see 36 ÷ 9, or 9 into 36, think immediately of 4. Don't go through the details of the process such as by saying "36 divided by 9 goes 4 times." Or when adding, like 5 + 11 + 8, you just slow yourself up if you say "5 plus 11 makes 16, plus 8 makes 24." Instead, just think: "16, 24." **Think short**. In the long run, you'll be that whiz-kid yet!

Omit words of a process as much as possible and concentrate on results. Work problems faster without words.

Numbers and calculating are like reciting the alphabet and reading. When you see a word, you don't stop to spell out the letters that make it up; you recognize the word at once in its entirety. Nor do you stop to consider each word separately; you read words together and think of what they mean as a whole doing the same with numbers and calculations will enable you to solve problems faster and easier.

Combining Mental and Written Math for Best Results

Short-cuts are not just a way of solving problems in your mind and in a flash, although they can help you do this. Taking the time to jot things down can often speed them up. Consider the following:

Calculating involves the mind in two processes: thinking out each step in the problem, and (2) remembering the results of each step for use in succeeding steps. Naturally, the longer the problem and the more complex, the more you have to recall if you do it entirely by mental math, and the more chances there are of making a mistake. On the other hand, if you work out the whole problem on paper, you don't have to keep remembering the results of steps and you can concentrate on the solution. Writing it down may take longer but it reduces the likelihood of error, and this can save time in the long run.

You can often achieve the maximum of speed with accuracy by using both the mental and the written methods. You do this by writing down the results of the various steps but not the details of the steps. For example: to multiply 49,837 by 11, there is no need to write out the whole problem or to struggle with it as a mental exercise; just write the partial products, then add to get the answer, thus: **(or use Short Cut#8)**

$$\begin{array}{r} 49837 \\ \underline{49837} \\ 548207 \end{array}$$

Or, if you want to divide 2,184 by 24, you might divide by 3 and write down 728 so you don't have to remember it; then divide by 8 to get the answer, 91.

Some Short-Cuts in this book will enable you to solve problems mentally and even on sight; others will work better if you write down partial results by steps; still other short-cuts will serve you best if you do the problem entirely on paper. It's up to you to determine how much to carry in your head and how much to write down in order to achieve both speed and accuracy. While speed is desirable, a short-cut to the wrong answer is obviously useless. It pays to take a longer route, if necessary, to reach the right answer the first time.

Is there an easy way to add large columns of numbers?

One of the casualties of our business-machine age is the bookkeeper of a few decades past who sat on a high stool, wore a green eyeshade, and could do lightning-fast arithmetic in his head. A favorite pastime of these men was simultaneous three-column additions.

$$\begin{array}{r} 123 \\ 654 \\ +\underline{\ \ 987} \\ 1{,}764 \end{array}$$

This is an easy and rapid way to add three columns of figures at the same time. Take the top number (123) and add the units figure of the next lower number (4) to get 127. Then add the tens figure (5, which is really 50) to 127, giving 177. Next add the hundreds figure (6, or really 600) to 177, which yields 777. Then add the figure in the units column of the bottom row (7) to get 784; the tens figure (8) to get 864; and the hundreds figure (9) to get 1,764. Once you have learned this trick, you can run down such a column of figures, noting the successive sums as you go: 123, 127, 177, 777, 784, 864, and 1,764. Of course, you can run up as well as down just as readily and the sum will be just as correct.

Writing down such a sum with little apparent effort never ceases to amaze the uninitiated. You can use a bit of trickery, however, to produce an even greater effect. Ask a friend to write a number having about five or six digits and then you write a similar number directly underneath it. Be sure, however, that your number and his are related as follows:

284,343	(friend's number)
710,657	(your number)

Starting with the left-hand side (to look casual) select each digit so that when added to the one above, the sum is 9. Do this until you reach the last digit and select this one to yield 10. (As you can see, this process gives 1,000,000). Then have your friend write another number and follow the same technique with your number. Repeat this process several times and when your last turn comes up, write down any figures at all so long as the sums are less than 9.

```
   369,247
   630,753
   473,291
   526,709
   974,531
    25,469
   425,823
 + 123,022
 3,548,845
```

To add the column start at the left and put down a 3, since there are 3 pairs of 1,000,000's above. Then simply add the last two rows, setting down the figures in their proper order. This trick will go over very well if you don't repeat it too often.

EXERCISE 19

Square each numbers using the TTFM, (on Page 23.3) and then multiply the answer by its original number

1. 688	4. 65782	7. 988	10. 1849
2. 20793	5. 747	8. 166	11. 418
3. 674	6. 294	9. 289	12. 668

EXERCISE 20

Square These Figures the **Supreme Way** (Page **16.**11)

1. 268	4. 56713	7. 456	10. 951	13. 629
2. 5639	5. 869	8. 438	11. 843	14. 6853
3. 562	6. 513	9 482	12. 687	15. 888

EXERCISE 21

Try your Hand with the **Boom-e-rang** (Page **5.**9)

1. 45 x 29	4. 65 x 78	7. 98 x 68	10. 78 x 49	13. 91 x 62
2. 77 x 74	5. 74 x 37	8. 46 x 16	11. 41 x 28	14. 67 x 53
3. 67 x 45	6. 29 x 14	9. 28 x 29	12. 66 x 58	15. 99 x 67

Here's a Handy Method to Multiply

When both numbers end in 5, add average tens digits and divide by 2, (a + b)/2, to the product of the tens (ab). Multiply the result by 100 and stick on 25 to complete the answer.

E.g., 85 x 45: 8 x 4 = 32. Average of (8 + 4) ÷ 2 = 6;
answer is computed as: 32 + 6 = 38 x 100 = 3800 + 25 = 3825.

Try another one: 65 x 35 = ?
6 x 3 = 18; (6 + 3 = 9)/2 = 4.5 = 18 + 4.5 = 22.5 x 100 = + 25 = 2275.

Check your friends' "Number Sense"

Tell your friends, "Betcha' that you can't count! G'wan, I'll betcha."

"OK, let's try an experiment. I'll start counting. I'll give you the first number, then you give me the next number plus one. Then it'll be my turn, then yours, then mine. We go on until one of us makes a mistake. Alright?"

Naturally, they agree. Then you start:
"What number comes after four thousand ninety-three?"
They will say: "Four thousand ninety-four."
You return with: "Four thousand ninety-five."
They say: "Four thousand ninety-six."
You say: "Four thousand ninety-seven."
They shout: "Four thousand ninety-eight."
You : "Four thousand ninety-nine."
They will automatically say: "Five thousand."
You: "Gotcha! Wrong! The answer is Four thousand one hundred!"

If people get into a reciting of numbers and don't keep their wits about them, they very easily fall into such a trap as this. Pull this on your friends just the one time. They'll thump you if you try it again.

I CALL THIS... MATH OF A HUNDRED CUTS ... READ ON AND YOU'LL GET THE POINT, SO TO SPEAK!

Chapter 22

Math of a Hundred Cuts!

"A Hundred Short Cuts, That Is!"

All Short Cuts have been amassed from countless sources, so if you recognize a few, they could already be in the school system, and then again, perhaps not. There are quite a few new ones mixed into this book.

Short Cut 1: When multiplying or dividing, initially disregard any following zeros. Then add on, if necessary, upon completing calculation.

Short Cut 2: When multiplying or dividing, ignore any decimal point. Then replace, if necessary, upon completing calculation.

Short Cut 3: To multiply a number by 4, double the number, and then double once more.

Short Cut 4: To divide a number by 4, halve the number, and then halve once more.

Short Cut 5: To multiply a number by 5, divide by 2, add 0.

Short Cut 6: To divide a number by 5, multiply by 2, add 0.

Short Cut 7: To square a number that ends in 5, multiply the tens digit by the next whole number, and then add on the 25. Eg., $35^2 = 3 \times (3 + 1 = 4) = 12\ 25$.

Short Cut 8: To multiply a two-digit number by 11, add a zero to each end of number, then start adding number to its right-hand neighbor. Eg.:0 5674 0 x 11 = (mentally) – add 4, 0 = **4**; add 7, 4 = 1**1**; add 6, 7 = 13 + 1=1**4**; add 5, 6 = 11 + 1 = 12; add 0 +5+1= 6. Answer: **62414.** Try several test numbers .

Short Cut 9: To multiply a number by 25, divide by 4.

Short Cut 10: To divide a number by 25, multiply by 4.

Short Cut 11: To multiply by 9 – Number x 10 less number.

Short Cut 12: To multiply by 12, double the number and add the neighbor (see Short Cut No. 8). Same logic here as there.

Short Cut 13: To multiply a number by 15, multiply the number by 10 and add half of the product.

Short Cut 14: To multiply two 2-digit numbers with tens digits the same and ones digits add to 10, multiply tens digit by next whole number, and add on product of the ones digits.

Short Cut 15: To multiply a one- or two-digit number by 99, subtract 1 from number and add on the difference between 100 and the number. Eg., 27x99 –>27–1=26; 100–27=73. Ans: 2673.

Short Cut 16: To multiply a one- or two-digit number by 101, write the number twice; if a one-digit number, insert a zero in the middle. 6 x 101 = 606; 29 x 101 = 2929.

Short Cut 17: To multiply two numbers whose difference is 2, square the number in the middle and subtract 1.

Short Cut 18: To check multiplication, multiply digit sums of factors and compare with digit sum of product. To check division, treat as multiplication, and check in same manner.

Short Cut 19: To multiply a number by 125, divide by 8.

Short Cut 20: To divide a number by 125, multiply by 8.

Short Cut 21: To multiply a number by 1.5, 2.5, etc., take half the number and then double the 1.5 (3.0). Then multiply.

Short Cut 22: To divide a number by 1.5, 2.5, etc., double both the number and the 1.5 (or 2.5, or similar nos.). Then divide.

Short Cut 23: To square a two-digit number beginning in 5, add 25 to the ones digit and add on the square of ones digit.

Short Cut 24: To square a two-digit number ending in 1, use the following example: $31^2 = 30^2 + 30 + 31 = 961$.

Short Cut 25: To multiply two 2-digit numbers without showing work, multiply ones digits together, then "cross-multiply," then multiply tens digits together. Carry if need be.

Short Cut 26: To multiply two numbers with difference of 4, square the number exactly in the middle and subtract 4.

Short Cut 27: If you can't calculate easily, try dividing one number in two smaller ones. For example, 6 x 18 as 6 x 9 x 2.

Short Cut 28: Guesstimate multiplication by 33 or 34, divide by 3.

Short Cut 29: Guesstimate division by 33 or 34, multiply by 3.

Short Cut 30: Guesstimate multiplication by 49 or 51, divide by 2.

Short Cut 31: Guesstimate division by 49 or 51, multiply by 2.

Short Cut 32: Guesstimate 66 times 67, multiply by 23.

Short Cut 33: Guesstimate division by 66 or 67, multiply by 1.5.

Short Cut 34: To estimate division by 9, multiply by 11.

Short Cut 35: To estimate division by 11, multiply by 9.

Short Cut 36: To estimate division by 14, multiply by 7.

Short Cut 37: To estimate division by 17, multiply by 6.

Short Cut 38: To multiply two numbers just over 100, start the 5-digit answer with a 1. Add on the sum, then the product of the ones digits. Eg.,104 x 102 = 1 (4 + 2 = 06) 4 x 2 = 08. Ans. 10608.

Short Cut 39: To subtract rapidly, look at subtraction as an addition, and work from left to right.

Short Cut 40: To subtract when numbers are on opposite sides of 100, 200, or higher, determine the two number and add them.

Eg.: 165 – 94= (65 above, and 6 below)(65 + 6 =) 71 answer.

Short Cut 41: When adding columns of numbers, enter the column total without carrying, moving one column to the left each time.

Short Cut 42: To mentally add a column of numbers, add one number at a time—first the tens digit, then the ones digit.

Short Cut 43: When adding long columns of numbers lightly cross out a digit every time you exceed 9, and proceed with just the ones digit.

Short Cut 44: When adding long columns of numbers, divide the column into smaller, more manageable sections.

Short Cut 45: When adding just a few numbers, it is fastest to begin with the largest number and to end with the smallest.

Short Cut 46: To add 1 + 2 + 3 + + n, multiply n by (n + 1), and then divide by 2.

Short Cut 47: If you prefer not to subtract by adding, you can subtract in two steps—first the tens digits, then the ones.

Short Cut 48: To check addition, use the 9's check system.

Short Cut 49: To check subtraction, add the answer upwards.

Short Cut 50: To multiply number by 75, multiply no. by 3/4.

Short Cut 51: To divide by 75, multiply number by 1-1/3.

Short Cut 52: To divide a number by 8, multiply no. by 1-1/4.

Short Cut 53: To divide number by 15, multiply no. by 2/3.

Short Cut 54: When multiplication seems slightly beyond your grasp, regroup, as in the following example: 43 x 6 = (40 x 6) + (3 x 6) = 258.

Short Cut 55: When a multiplicand or multiplier is just near a multiple of 10 or 100, round up and subtract, as in the following example: 15 x 29 = (15 x 30) – (15x 1) = 435

Short Cut 56: To multiply a 3-digit or larger number by 11, first carry down the ones digit of the number. Then add the ones and tens digits, the tens and hundreds digit, and so forth.

Short Cut 57: Dividing by all nines produces a repeating pattern. For example, 2 ÷ 9 = 0.222....., 47 ÷ 99 = 0.474747....., and 588 ÷ 999 = 0.588588588....

Short Cut 58: Boomerang 1 – To multiply any two digits in the tens value of 11 to 19, add upper figure to lower ones digit and add zero. Next, multiply ones digits (vertically) and add to first total. Eg., 19 x 12 = 19 + 2 = 21(0) or 210.
9 x 2 = 18. 210 + 18 = 228.

Short Cut 59: Boomerang 2 – To multiply any two digits in the tens value of 29 to 11, add upper figure to lower ones digit and add zero. Next, multiply ones digits (vertically) and add 1 unit digit to first total. Eg., **29** x **14** = 29 + 4 = **33**(0). 9 x 4 = **36**. Save that **6**. 330 + 6 = 336. The 3 of **36** is added to the 4 of **14** = **7**(0) in tens sense. Answer is 336 + **70** = 406.

Short Cut 60: To square any numbers, the rule of thumb is to designate the letters a, b, c, d, e, etc., to the number from left to right. 478^2 is then represented as:

a b c
4 7 8

to compute, use this thinking:

$\underline{c^2} + \underline{(2)bc} + \underline{(2)ac + b^2} + \underline{(2)ab} + \underline{a^2}$

or: write from right to left, **64**, 7 x 8 = 56 x 2 = 112 + 6 = 11**8,** 4 x 8 x 2 = 64 + 7^2 (49) = 11**3** + 11 = 12**4,** (2) 4 x 7 = 56 + 12 = 6**8,** 4^2 = 16 + 6 = **22.**

Answer: 228,484. It might look hard, but it's all over in a few seconds. Try it, you'll like it! If you square 3 digits, 4 digits, and higher, your speed at doing squares will be phenomenal.

Short Cut 61: To multiply a number by 98, multiply by 100, and subtract twice the given number.

Short Cut 62: To multiply a number by 102, multiply by 100, and add twice the given number.

Short Cut 63: To determine the number of decimal places in the product, add the number of decimal places in the numbers being multiplied.

Short Cut 64: To add or subtract fractions:
1. – find the lowest common denominator (LCD) for all the fractions in the questions.
2. – rewrite each fraction as an equivalent fraction, using this denominator.
3. – add or subtract the denominator.

Short Cut 65: To add or subtract mixed numbers:
1. – add or subtract the whole numbers,
2. – add or subtract the factions,
3. – add together the results of the above.

Short Cut 66: To multiply fractions, multiply the numerators and divide by the product of the denominators. (Eg., 2/3 x 4/5 = 2 x 4 / 3 x 5 = 8/15; 5/7 x 3/5 = 5 x 3 / 7 x 5 = 15/35 = 3/7.)

Short Cut 67: To multiply mixed numbers, use the mixed numbers as improper fractions (eg., 1-1/8 x 3/7 = 9/8 x 3/7 = 27/56) and multiply as you would proper fractions. *(An improper fraction is one where the numerator is larger than the denominator.)*

Short Cut 68: To multiply mixed numbers, use the mixed numbers as improper fractions (eg., 1-1/8 x 3/7 = 9/8 x 3/7 = 27/56) and multiply as you would proper fractions.

Short Cut 69: To multiply a fraction by a whole number, rewrite the whole number as a fraction with denominator of 1, multiply as you normally do with proper fractions. (5/8 x 2 = 5/8 x 2/1 = 10/8 = 1-2/8 = 1-1/4).

Short Cut 70: To divide by a fraction, multiply by its reciprocal. (5/8 ÷ 2/5 = 5/8 x 5/2 = 25/16 = 1-9/16.)

Short Cut 71: To change a fraction to a decimal, divide the numerator by the denominator. (3/5 = 3 ÷ 5 = 0.6)

Short Cut 72: To change a decimal fraction into a common fraction, use the number without the decimal point as the numerator. The denominator is 1 followed by as many zeros as there are to the right of the decimal point. (0.25 = 25/100 = 1/4)

Short Cut 73: To change a per cent to a fraction, divide by 100 and drop the per cent sign. (60% = 60/100 = 3/5.)

Short Cut 74: To change a fraction to a per cent, multiply by 100. (4/5 = 4/5 x 100% = 80%.)

Short Cut 75: To change a per cent to a decimal, divide the rate per cent by 100. (35% = 35/100 = 0.35; 139% = 139/100 = 1.39)

Short Cut 76: To change a decimal to a per cent, multiply the decimal by 100%. (0.35 = 0.35 x 100% = 35%; 1.39 = 1.39 x 100% = 139%)

Review of Algebraic Short Cuts

Short Cut 77: To multiply powers having the same base, add the indices. (3^2 – 3 is the base, 2 is the index; a^4 is the 4th power of a. Eg.: 3 x 3 x 3 x 3 = 3^4 = 81.) So a x a x a x a = a^4.

Short Cut 78: To divide a power having the same base, subtract the indices. ($a^6b^5 \div 3a^2b^2$ gives the remainder of $3a^4b^3$.)

Short Cut 79: To reduce an algebraic expression to its simplest form treat the order of operations in the bracket in the following manner divide, multiply, add, and last, subtract.

Short Cut 80: To multiply a polynomial by a monomial, multiply each term of the polynomial by the monomial. (*A polynomial is an expression containing two or more terms. Monomial expresses only one term.)*

Short Cut 81: To divide a polynomial, locate the highest common factor of each term in the polynomial and divide same by that factor. Write down the monomial factor, followed by the second factor in brackets.

Short Cut 82: If the same number is added to or subtracted from each side of equation, then the equation stays in balance.

Short Cut 83: If both sides of an equation are multiplied or divided by the same number, equation stays in same balance.

Short Cut 84: To multiply a polynomial by a monomial, multiply each term of the polynomial by the monomial.

Short Cuts 85 through 100:

How to tell if a number is divisible by:

2 – If it is an even number, i. e. ends in 2,4,6,8,or 0.

3 – If the sum of the digits of the number is divisible by 3.

4 – If the last two digits of the number represents a number that is divisible by 4.

6 – If the number meets the tests for 2 and 3.

8 – If the last three digits of the number represents a number divisible by 8.

9 – If the sum of the digits of the number is divisible by 9.

5 – If the number ends in 0 or 5.

10 – If the number ends in 0.

*11– Find the sum of the digits in even place-value powers of ten.
Find the sum of the digits in odd place value powers of ten. If the difference of these two sum is divisible by 11, the number is then divisible by 11.

12 – If the numbers meet the above tests for 3 and 4.

*11 – 10^5, 10^4, 10^3, 10^2, 10^1, 10^0. The even and odd place-value powers refer to the exponents – 0, 1, 2, 3, 4, 5, 6, on & on.

Note: If you need extra copies for your family, friends, gifts, etc., contact your Book Stores in your neighborhood. If there are no outlets to accommodate you, contact:
Algotext Publishers at: 33 Orlando Boulevard, Scarborough, Ont., Canada M1R 3N5 Fax: (416) 444-5044 (Send money order ($10.95) plus $1.50 extra for H & S.

YOU GUESSED
IT....OUR
SUBJECT IS
MULTIPLYING

Chapter 23

Multiplying in a Hurry!

Here is the long-awaited re-awakening of the Trachtenberg *Speed Method for Basic Arithmetic!* This method multiplies large numbers by any single-digit number. Except for the rules prescribed for Short Cuts No. 8 and No. 85 - 100, these new procedures will not take too long before you're in charge of Multiplication.

It is understood in the following lines that the **"number"** is that digit of the multiplicand just above the place where the next digit of the answer will appear, and the "neighbor" is the digit immediately to the right of the "number." When there is no neighbor (at the right-hand end of the given number), the neighbor is zero – it is ignored. But always imagine a zero is to be placed in front of the multiplicand to remind us that a digit of the answer could appear there. **"N" – for Neighbor.**

TO MULTIPLY BY	THE PROCEDURE IS AS FOLLOWS:
11	Add the neighbor. (See Short Cut 8)
12	Double the number and add the neighbor.
6	**Add 5 to the number if the number is odd;** add nothing even. Add "half" the neighbor (**N**) (drop fractions). If a 7, add a 5 = 12 + 1/2 **N.**
7	Double the number and **add 5 if the number is odd,** and add "half" the neighbor.
5	Use "half" the neighbor, **plus 5 if the number is odd.**

9 First step: subtract from 10.
Middle steps: subtract from 9 and add the neighbor.
Last step: reduce left-hand digit of multiplicand by 1.

8 First step: subtract from 10 and double.
Middle steps: subtract from 9, double, and add the neighbor.
Last step: reduce left-hand digit of multiplicand by 2.

4 First step: subtract from 10, and **add 5 if the number is odd.**
Middle steps: subtract from 9 and add "half" the neighbor, **plus 5 if the number is odd.**
Last step: take "half" the left-hand of the multiplicand and reduce by 1.

3 First step: subtract from 10 and double, and **add 5 if the number is odd.**
Middle steps: subtract from 9 and double, **add 5 if the number is odd,** and add "half" the neighbor.
Last step: take "half" the left-hand digit of the multiplicand and reduce by 2.

2 Double each digit of the multiplicand without using the neighbor at all.

1 Copy down the multiplicand unchanged.

0 Zero times any number at all is zero.

(Please put these rules for High-Speed Rapid Calculation to memory – Their importance is the greatest test of your math Number Sense available. Better known as the Trachtenberg Method, the works of Jakow Trachtenberg are required reading. Check your Librarian for his books, and if they're missing or stolen, ask or pressure for the book to put back into circulation!

High Speed Multiplication

Better known as the T-T-F-M (Trachtenberg Two-Finger Method)

The Trachtenberg High-Speed concept, in brief, uses the two-finger method consisting of these three features:

(This technique offers "Amazing" speed as your goal. You can multiply two sets of numbers, as wide as 12 by 10 numbers. Recently, in Europe, a 14-year-old confounded a group of mathematicians with such a feat – and did it in a blazing 72 seconds' time. Try this, you,ll love it! Remember, when you are using the two-finger system, it's not required to have hands on after a few successful try-outs. You can stand back and do it from afar. The easiest way I learned to do it is to place a small pencil mark over the left hand numbers as I'm mentally moving the calculations from right to left.

1. This is the process of forming pair-products, such as the pair-product 9 is formed out of 4 9 times 6:

```
U T
4 9   x   6
2(4) (5)4
 4 + 5
   9      the pair-product
```

2. Then there is a way of multiplying any number by a single digit using these pair-products:

```
        U T
0 8 6 4 9  x  6
        4          the units of 9 times 6 is 54 is 4

       UT
0 8 6 4 9  x  6
      9 4          9 is the pair-product of 4 9
                   times 6
```

continuing on until finally we reach

```
U T
0 8 6 4 9  x  6
5 1 8 9 4
```

3. There is a neat way of extending this multiplication by a single digit that could include multiplication by numbers of any length. Try forming several pair-products and adding them to find each digit of the answer. These several pair-products are called "inner" and "outer" pairs, taken by moving inward from both ends toward the space between the two numbers being multiplied:

THREE-DIGIT + (the TTFM Method)

More often than not, the larger numbers keep popping up. So we may well do the worst possible calculation. But let's take our time working up to that speed. Each time a number is worked on, it expands the answer to its final answer. It may seem slow at first when you're breaking into the method. You will work on each factor individually. The answer is arrived at in a working out on digit-pair, by using the new but later on, the usual units-and tens idea. Let us look at an example, 263 times 145. We must put 3 zeroes in front (145 has 3 digits!).

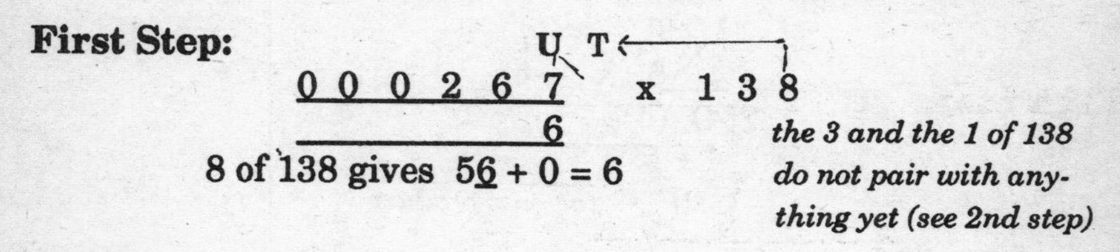

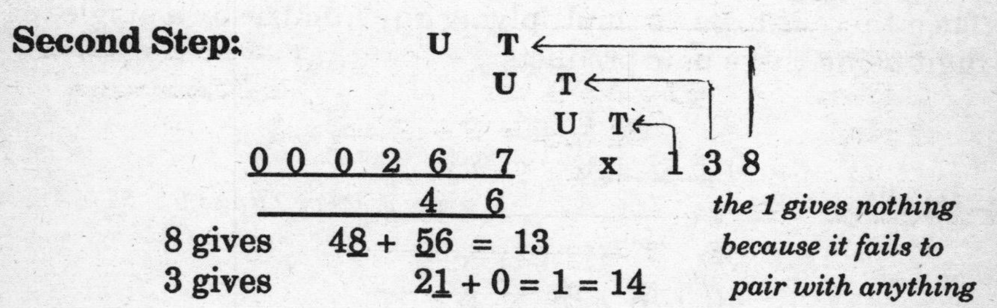

In fact, if you compare this with the preceding example you will find the work so far has been the same. That is because the 1 of 138 has not yet contributed to the answer – it has not yet paired with any part of the 267. But now we go on:

Third Step:

```
U  T ←──────────────┐
   U  T ←────────┐  │
      U  T ←──┐  │  │
0 0 0 2  6  7    x   1 3 8
        8  4  6
```

underlined figures add to 27 + the dot makes it 28

8 gives 16 + 48 = 10
3 gives 18 + 21 = 10
1 gives 07 + 0 = 7

Fourth Step:

```
U  T ←──────────────┐
   U  T ←────────┐  │
      U  T ←──┐  │  │
0 0 0  2 6 7     x   1 3 8
     6  8  4  6
```

8 gives 0 + 16 = 1
3 gives 06 + 18 = 7
1 gives 06 + 07 = 6 + 2 dots = 16

The 8 is not out of action – it still gives the tens-digit of 8 times 2 = 16 .

Fifth Step:

```
U  T ←──────────────┐
   U  T ←────────┐  │
      U  T ←──┐  │  │
0 0 0  2  6  7    x   1 3 8
  3  6  8  4  6
```

the 8 is out of action, its UT hits zeroes

8 gives 0 + 0
3 gives 02 + 0 = 0
1 gives 02 + 06 = 2 + 1(dot) = 3

Sixth Step:

```
U  T ←──────────────┐
   U  T ←────────┐  │
      U  T ←──┐  │  │
0 0 0  2  6  7    x   1 3 8
  3  6  8  4  6
```

the 8 is out of action, its UT hits zeroes

8 gives 0 + 0
3 gives 02 + 0 = 0
1 gives 02 + 06 = 2 + 1(dot) = 3

Last Step:

```
          U T
    0 0 0 2 6 7      x  1 3 8
    0 3 6 8 4 6
1 gives        00 + 00 =  0
```

The answer is 36,846. As you can now see, 8 digits by 8 digits is extremely simple. As I mentioned earlier, a young student in Europe multiplied the large number: 5132437201 times 452736502785 in seventy plus seconds! By using this high-speed technique. Anything is possible when you apply yourself.

EXERCISE 22

This is new to you, so pay attention, please.

When you do these problems, say out-loud the pair-product of the pair numbers, then check your answers at back of book. Do the single-digit multiplications first, so you get into the habit of just speaking the Units' value first and then mentally adding the Tens' value to it for that two-some's answer.

EXERCISE 22

1. 58 x 6	3. 79 x 4	5. 78 x 9	7. 57 x 4	9. 58 x 8
2. 33 x 7	4. 86 x 8	6. 34 x 7	8. 99 x 9	10. 61 x 9

Now we'll raise the sights a little higher.

11. 78 x 45	13. 113 x 12	15. 345 x 67	17. 2347 x 116
12. 93 x 68	14. 456 x 69	16. 8475 x 39	18. 73645 x 117

Well, there you've done it! I hope you flourish, succeed, and enjoy your future in the Realm Of Mathematics. The country needs Scientists, Mathematicians, Business people who have the smarts to enrich their professions and pass the torch of Learning to their children. Long live our Freedom from want and closed minds!

Glossary – PART ONE

Abacus – an instrument with sliding counters on parallel wires, each wire representing one place in the numeration system.

Acute angle – an angle that measures less than 90 degrees.

Algorithm – a pencil-and-paper procedure for computation, showing the steps involved.

Analog clock – a timepiece that indicates the time through the position of its hands.

Area – surface measure of a plane region (expressed in square units)

Array -- an orderly arrangement of objects or symbols into rows and columns eg. 66.45
9.33

Associative property -- of addition: (2 + 3) + 4 = 2 + (3 + 4)
-- of multiplication: (2 x 3) x 4 = 2 x (3 x 4)

Attribute -- a quantitative or qualitative characteristic of an object or shape. (e.g., colour, size, thickness)

Attribute blocks -- a set of blocks that have different characteristics, such as colour, shape, size, and thickness.

Bar graph – a graph that uses either vertical or horizontal bars to indicate relationships among data.

Base ten blocks – a set of blocks designed to represent one cube, ten cubes, one hundred cubes, and one thousand cubes.

Basic facts – all the single-digit addition and multiplication facts (i.e., up to 9 + 9 and 9 x 9) and their inverse of subtraction (to 18 - 9) and division (to 81 ÷ 9).

Broken line graph – a graph in which points on a grid are joined with line segments.

Capacity – a measure indicating how much a container can hold, usually referring to liquid measure.

Cardinal number – the number of elements in a set (used to answer the question "How many?").

Centicubes – a commercial product consisting of interlocking 1 cm x 1cm x 1cm cubes, each of which has a mass of 1g

Circumference – the distance around a circle.

Commutative property – of addition: 2 + 3 = 3 + 2
of multiplication: 2 x 3 = 3 x 2

Composite number – a whole number greater than 1 that has factors other than 1 and itself. (e.g., 6)

Concrete representional graph – a graph which real objects are used to represent

Congruent – having the same size and shape.

Conservation *(constancy, invariance)* – the property of something remaining the same despite changes such as physical rearrangement.

Coordinates – a pair of numbers that give the location of a point on a plane.

Cuisenaire rods – a collection of related coloured blocks in ten different lengths, each of a corresponding colour.

Denominator – the number below the fraction bar in a fraction (e.g., 2/**3**).

Diameter – a line segment passing through the centre of a circle that divides the circle into 2 semi-circles.
e.g., (draw large circle and indicate equator , showing 2 hemispheres)

Difference – the answer in a subtraction problem.

Digit – a single number symbol. (e.g., 0, 1, 2, 3, 4)

Digital clock – a timepiece that shows the time in a row of digits.

Distributive property of multiplication –
3 x (4 + 5) = (3 x 4) + (3 x 5).

Dividend – the number that is to be divided in a division problem.
e.g., 9) **1809**

Divisor – the number by which the dividend is to be divided in a division problem.
e.g., **9**) 1809

Dot paper – paper with dots in an array format.

Edge – a line along which 2 faces of a solid meet

Equation – mathematical sentence stating two expressions are equal.

Equivalent fractions – fractions that name same number
(e.g., 2/3, 4/6 and 8/12)

Equilateral triangle – a triangle with 3 equal sides and 3 equal angles

Estimation – the process of producing an answer that is not exact

Expanded notation – a method of writing a numeral as the sum of its place value components
(e.g., 5327 = 5000 + 300 +20 +7)

Faces – a plane surface of a geometric solid
(e.g., a cube has 6 squares as faces)

Factor – a number that can be divided evenly into the given number

e.g., The factors of 72 are 1, 2, 3, 4, 6, 8, 24, 72
(1 & 72, exceptions) .

Flip – an action in motion geometry that produces a mirror

Fraction bar – the line segment drawn horizontally or diagonally between the numerator and denominator of a fraction

e.g., 1/2 or 2/3

GCF – (Greatest Common Factor) the greatest whole number that is a factor of each of two other numbers

(e.g., 6 is the GCF of 18 and 24)

Geoboard – a board with nails or pegs, usually in an array format

Geopaper – dot-paper with dots similar to the markings on a geoboard

Geometry – the study of space and shapes in space

Graph – a drawing designed to show relationships among data

Grid – a set of horizontal and vertical lines spaced uniformly

Hexagon – any polygon with 6 sides

Hundreds board or chart – a board or chart with the numerals 1 to 100 in a 10 x 10 array

Improper Fraction – a fraction having a numerator equal to or greater than the denominator

(e.g., 7/2, 3/3, 6/4)

Interlocking cubes – plastic cubes that interlock on one side

Inverse operation – an operation which reverses or does the opposite of another operation

– subtraction is the inverse of addition
– division is the inverse of multiplication

Isosceles triangle – a triangle having 2 sides of the same length and 2 angles of the same size

LCM – (Least Common Multiple) the smallest whole number that is a multiple of each of two other numbers (e.g., 7 is the LCM of 14 and 21)

Line – a straight path that extends infinitely in both directions

Line segment – a straight path that connects two endpoints

Logic blocks – see "attribute blocks"

Many-to-one correspondence – the matching of elements in two set (e.g., 3 pennies to each pocket)

Metric mass – the quantity of matter in an object (commonly referred to as "weight")

Metric system – a system of measurement based on the decimal system

Metronome – an instrument designed to mark exact time by a regularly repeated tick, usually used in music

Minuend – the number from which a number is subtracted

$$\begin{array}{r} 43 \\ \text{e.g.}\quad \underline{-\,26} \end{array}$$

Mixed number – (number that consists of a whole number and a fraction, (e.g., 2 3/4)

Motion geometry – the study of the movement of shapes; also referred to transformational geometry

Multiples – the products obtained by multiplying a whole number by a given factor (e.g., the multiples of 10 are 10, 20, 30, 40, 50 etc.)

Net – a pattern for a geometric solid e.g., draw 2 bandaids at right angles

Non-standard unit – an arbitrary unit of measurement

Non-unit fractions – fractions with numerator greater than 1 (e.g., 3/4, 7/8)

Number – a mathematical concept that indicates quantity (i.e., how many in a set)

Number sentence – a statement involving numbers (e.g., 3 + 15 = 18)

Numeral – a written symbol used to represent a number (e.g., 5)

Numeration system – a system that uses symbols to express s numbers

Numerator – the number above the fraction bar in a fraction

Numeric dating – a method of recording the date using only numerals
(e.g., 19 09 1989)

Obtuse angle – an angle __ measuring more than 90°

Octagon – a polygon with 8 sides
(e.g., a stop sign is an octagon)

One-to-one – matching of elements in two sets one-to-one (similar)
(e.g., one lid to each jar)

Oral counting – the recitation of number words in sequence

Ordinal number – a number that indicates the position of an item in an ordered set
(e.g., sixth, seventh, tenth)

palindrome – a numeral that reads the same backward as forward
(e.g., 323)

Parallelogram – a quadrilateral with both pairs of opposite sides parallel

Pattern blocks – a set of commercially–made blocks of 6 shapes, each of a standard colour

Pentagon – a polygon with 5 sides

Pentomino – any arrangement of 5 congruent squares in which whole sides match

Perimeter – the distance around the outside of a plane figure

Pictograph – a graph in which pictures are used to represent data

Place value – value assigned to each position in a numeral

Plane geometry – the study of two–dimensional shapes

Plane shape – a two–dimensional figure

Point – a position on a line or line segment ——·——

Polygon – a simple, closed plane figure having 3 or more sides

Polyhedron – a three–dimensional shape with many faces, all of which are polygons (plural, polyhedra)

Prime number – number greater than 1 with only itself and 1 as factors (e.g., 2, 3, 5, 7, 11, 13)

Prism – a polyhedron with 2 congruent parallel faces called the bases, with all other faces being parallelograms

Product – the answer to a multiplication problem

Program – a series of instructions written in a computer language to accomplish a certain task

Proper fraction – a fraction in which the numerator is less than the denominator
(e.g., 2/3,1/2, 3/10)

Property – characteristic common to all members of a class

Protractor – an instrument used for measuring angles

Pyramid – a polyhedron in which one face (the base) is a polygon and the other faces are triangles with a common vertex.
(Each pyramid is named for the shape of its base.)

Quadrilateral – a four–sided polygon

Quotient – the answer in a division problem

Radius – a line segment extending from centre of a circle to any point on the circle

Ray – a line segment with just one end–point · ———>

Real graph – a graph made from the actual objects under consideration

Reciprocals – pair of fractional numbers whose product is 1
(e.g., 3/4 and 4/3; 3/4 x 4/3 = 1)

Rectangular prism – a box–shaped solid, the faces of which are all rectangles

Regrouping – the process used in changing a unit from one place value to another
(e.g., 42 can be regrouped to 3 tens and 12 ones)

Regular polygon – a polygon in which all sides are equal and all angles are equal in measure

Rhombus – a parallelogram with all sides of equal length

Rotation – see turn

Rotational symmetry – see symmetry

Rote memorization – process of memorizing information or rule without an understanding of the underlying meaning

Scalene triangle – a triangle in which all sides are different lengths

Set – a group of items

Similar/similarity – having the same shape but not necessarily the same size

Simplest form – the form in which a fraction is written if the numerator and denominator have no common factors other than 1

(e.g., 2/3, 6/7, 9/10)

Skip multiples – to count by multiples of a given number

(e.g., 3, 6, 9, 12...)

Slide – an action in motion geometry which moves a figure along parallel lines into another location (also called a translation)

Software – computer programs that indicate what operations the computer must perform

Solid – a three–dimensional shape

Solid geometry – the study of three-dimensional shapes

Sorting – the physical process of selecting and grouping all objects that possess a common attribute

Spatial visualization – the mental manipulation of objects in space

Subtrahend – a number to be subtracted from another number

e.g., 76
– **45**

Symmetry – a correspondence in size, shape, and relative position of parts on opposite sides of a dividing line (line symmetry) or about a centre (rotational symmetry)

Tangram – an old Chinese puzzle consisting of a square cut into triangles, 1 square and 1 parallelogram

Tessellation *(tiling)* – an arrangement of geometric shapes that fit together without spaces or overlaps
(Tiling) – see Tessellation

Trapezoid – a quadrilateral with one pair of opposite sides parallel

Turn – an action in motion geometry which moves a shape about a point (also called a rotation)

Unit – 1. the first whole number
2. a determined quantity used as a standard for measurement

Volume – the amount of space occupied by a three-dimensional object (expressed in cubic units)

Weight – a force with which gravity pulls on an object (commonly used to mean mass)

Whole numbers – numbers of the set (0, 1, 2, 3, 4, 5, . . .)

MATHEMATICAL TERMS – PART TWO

algorithm – method of calculation by the use of a detailed step- by-step procedure

arithmetic progression – sequence in which each number differs from the preceding one by a constant amount, such as *2, 5, 8, 11, 14 . . .*

binary – relating to a system of numbers having 2 as its base

calculus – branch of mathematics dealing with continuously changing quantities; method of calculation in which symbols are used

coefficient – numerical factor in an elementary algebraic term such as *3* in the term *3x*

congruent – referring to geometrical figures that coincide exactly in shape and size

constant – quantity retaining a fixed value throughout a series of calculations

coordinates – set of numbers used to determine the position of a point, line, or curve

denominator / divisor – quantity that is divided into another, quantity below the division line in a fraction

equation – mathematical statement in which two expressions or numbers are connected by an equal sign, such as $3x + 2y -17$

exponent / index / power – symbol indicating the number of times a quantity is to be multiplied by itself, such as ^{3} in $2^3 = 8$

factor – any of the quantities that can be divided into a given quantity exactly: 9 and 5 are factors of 45

factorial – product of all the whole numbers from a given number down to 1. Factorial 5 is 5 x 4 x 3 x 2 x 1 = 120

Fibonacci – infinite series of numbers, each of which is the sum of the preceding two

function – variable connected with another variable in such a way that a change in one produces a like or corresponding change in the other

geometrical progression – sequence of numbers in which each term is obtained by multiplying the preceding term by a constant factor, such as 2, 6, 18, 54, 162 . . .

integer – any whole number, positive or negative, together with zero

locus – path traced by a point, or surface that moves under stated conditions

logarithm / log – any one of a system of figures used in calculations, based on the number of times a base number, such as 10, has to be multiplied by itself to produce a given number

multiple – any of the quantities that a given number can be divided into exactly: 27, 45, 63, and so on are multiples of 9

numerator / dividend – quantity into which another is divided; quantity above the division line in a fraction

permutation – ordered arrangement of the quantities in a set into any of various possible groups

product – result of multiplying one quantity by another

Pythagorean theorem – theorem relating to the length of the sides of a right-angled triangle

quotient – result of dividing one quantity by another

rational number – number that can be expressed as a real whole number, or as a fraction involving two whole numbers

reciprocal / inverse – number obtained when another number is divided into 1

recurring decimal – decimal number ending in a pattern of one or more digits repeated indefinitely, as 0.87878787...

secant – straight line intersecting a curve at two or more points

tangent – line, curve, or surface touching but not cutting another

topology – geometry studying the properties of a figure or solid that remains unaffected even when the figure is stretched or twisted

trigonometry – study and application of the relationships involving the sides and angles of triangles, as used in surveying and navigation

variable – quantity that can assume any of the various possible values

variance – in statistics, a measure of the spread of a source of numbers or measurements

Geometric shapes: Solids, Other Solids, Angles and Circles

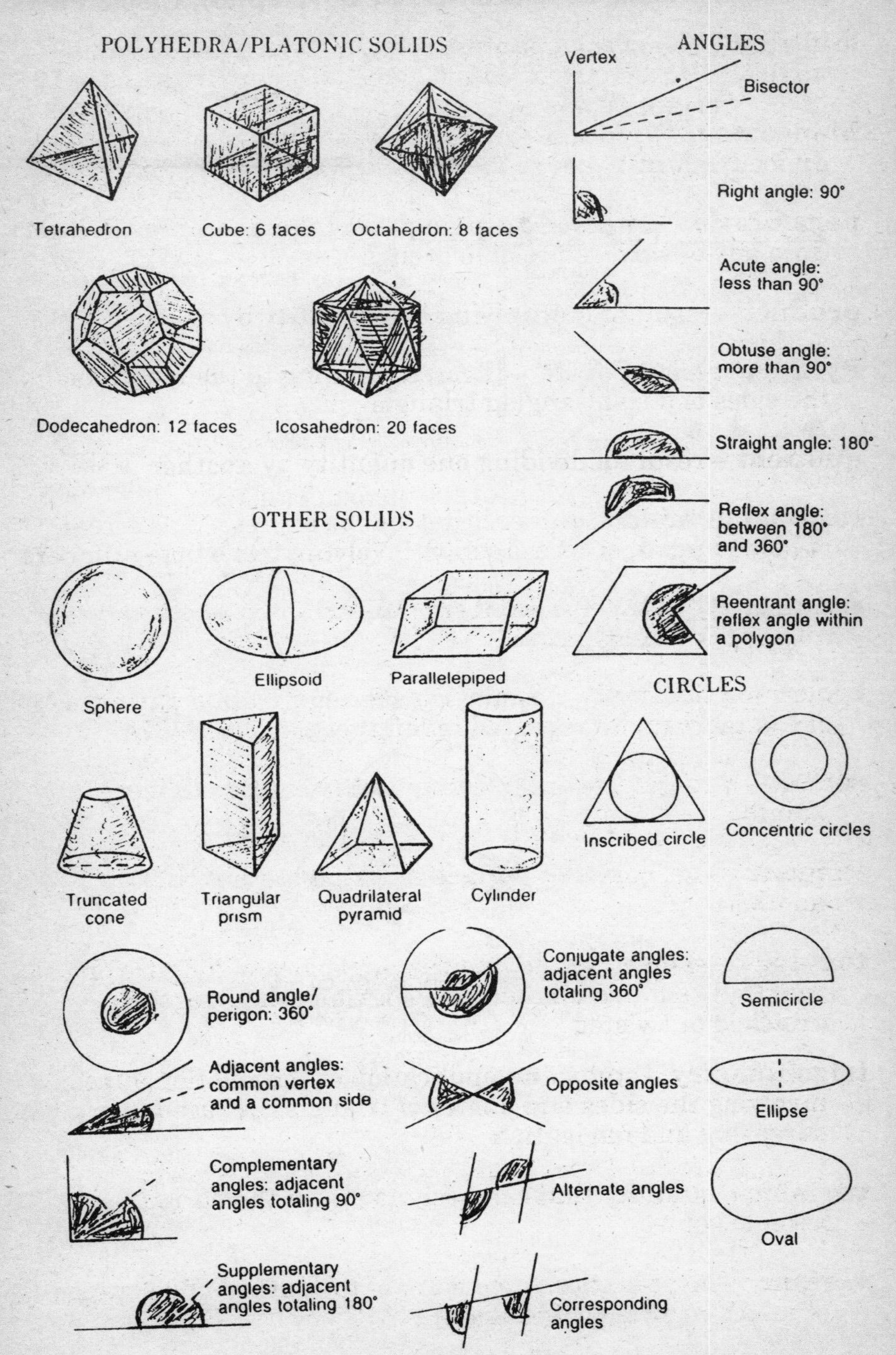

Geometric Shapes: Triangles, Polygons, Quadrilaterals Parallelograms, Gons (Penta-, Hexa-, Hepta-), Circle Parts

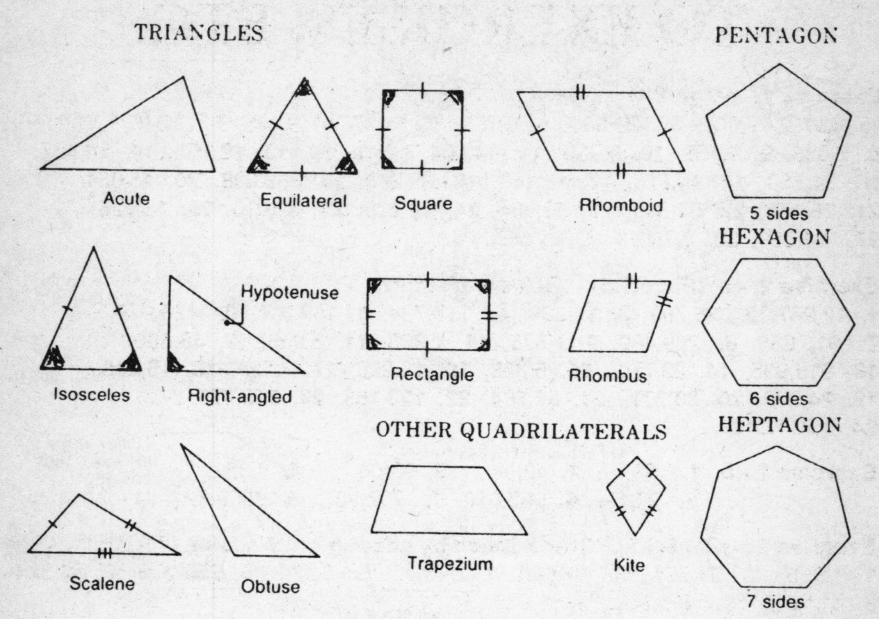

PARTS OF A CIRCLE

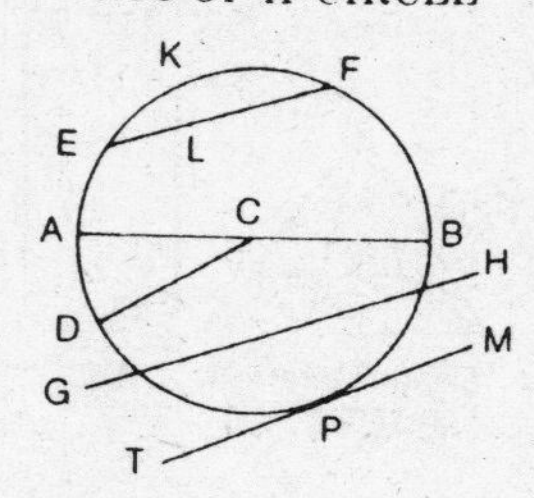

AB diameter. C center. CD, CA, CB radii.
EKF arc on EF chord. EFKL (area) segment on EF chord. ACD (area) sector.
GH secant. TPM tangent.
EKFBPDA circumference

ANSWERS TO EXERCISES, ETC.

Exercise 1. (Page 1.4)
1. 630 **2.** 7,300, **3.** 589,000, **4.** 6,798, **5.** 4,067, **6.** 3,245, **7.** 7,348, **8.** 6,665, **9.** 9,552, **10.** 9,735, **11.** 14,004, **12.** 5,054, **13.** 12,152, **14.** 14,477, **15.** 31,659, **16.** 44,625, **17.** 18,163, **18.** 32,305, **19.** 888,998, **20.** 45,854, **21.** 28,458, **22.** 37,389, **23.** 53,064, **24.** 48,228, **25.** 32,010, **26.** 13,725 **27.** 14,250, **28.** 8,700.

Exercise 2. - a (Page 1.6). Gelosia Method
1. 12,267, **2.** 25,709, **3.** 11,986, **4.** 117,734, **5.** 159,016, **6.** 128,979, **7.** 918,935, **8.** 209,480, **9.** 1,575, **10.** 1,323, **11.** 3,036, **12.** 48,600, **13.** 918,935, **14.** 29,770, **15.** 5,328, **16.** 16,226, **17.** 7,225, **18.** 16,218, **19.** 24,978, **20.** 83,271, **21.** 57,564, **22.** 123,165, **23.** 548,475, **24.** 1,211,310.

Exercise 2 - b. **1.** 63, **2.** 42, **3.** 9,408, **4.** 8,352, **5.** 9,312, **6.** 993,010, **7.** 992,007, **8.** 983,052

Exercise 3 – (Page 1.7). Check these by casting out 9's, and 11's.
1. 1,955, **2.** 31,777, **3.** 24,696 **4.** 18,321, **5.** 8,424, **6.** 739,293 **7.** 50,304 **8.** 114,938 **9.** 403,542 **10.** 1,629,750 **11.** 1,689,779 **12.** 4,637,550 **13.** 1,235,850 **14.** 3,681,454 **15.** 1,535,100. **16.** 12,186,984. **17.** $41.04 **18.** 28.56 **19.** 44,640 min. **20.** 10,395 lines **21.** 10,167,300 **22.** 211,322 miles **23.** 80. 5 **24.** 48 miles.

STAGE 1 – Exercise 4 A– Page 5.2
1. 266, **2.** 288, **3.** 323, **4.** 180, **5.** 176,
6. 204, **7.** 196, **8.** 270, **9.** 256, **10.** 361,
11. 144, **12.** 209, **13.** 224, **14.** 180, **15.** 342,
16. 221, **17.** 304, **18.** 238, **19.** 169, **20.** 324.

STAGE 2 – Exercise 4B– Page 5.4
1. 406, **2.** 312, **3.** 532, **4.** 264, **5.** 416,
6. 162, **7.** 336, **8.** 364, **9.** 368, **10.** 348,
11. 396, **12.** 289, **13.** 224, **14.** 315, **15.** 380,
16. 551, **17.** 286, **18.** 513, **19.** 350, **20.** 414.

STAGE 4 – Exercise 4C– Page 5.9
1. 4,004, **4.** 1,484, **7.** 4,263, **10.** 2,925,
2. 4,656, **5.** 3,239, **8.** 8,352, **11.** 1,449,
3. 3,612, **6.** 2,091, **9.** 2,592 **12.** 4,429

STAGE 4 – Exercise 5 – Page 5.14
1. 404, **4.** 3.906, **7.** 3,828, **10.** 4,275,
2. 4,464, **5.** 4,361, **8.** 7,968, **11.** 6,789,
3. 4,136, **6.** 3,731, **9.** 2,760 **12.** 5,859

Exercise 6 – Page 6.3

1. 625, **4.** 3,025, **7.** 225, **10.** 13,225,
2. 2,025, **5.** 9,025, **8.** 7,225, **11.** 11,025,
3. 5,625, **6.** 4,225, **9.** 15,625, **12.** 99,225

Exercise 7/8 – Page 6.4

Column D – when you've done, the cadence of units digits should read in this procession:
73, 81, 85, 89, 93, etc.,going on as ending 7, 1, 5, 9, 3, etc.
89, 93, 97, 101, 105, 109, continuing 3, 7, 1, 5, 9, etc.
98, 102 106, 110, 114, 118, continuing, 8, 2, 6, 0, 4, 8, etc.
14, 18, 22, 26, 30, 34, continuing, 8, 2, 6, 0, 4, etc.
You will notice that you can rattle these off in fast order. The greater the distance between the counting and reversing the sharper the brain becomes. Good work!

Exercise 9 – Page 9.3

Look for the repeating series of numbers, and also do it the "add 20, then add 6" method. It is always prudent to add and see the increment as an addition with number sense, but if you're planning an stage work, then the repeated wheel effect of a series of number properly scaled to each other makes you like a genius.Ho-hum! That's Show Biz.

Exercise 10 – Page 9.3

1. 19, **2.** 29, **3.** 69, **4.** 13, **5.** 15, **6.** 9, **7.** 26, **8.** 13.

Exercise 11 – Page 9.3

1. 109, **2.** 259, **3.** 599, **4.** 126, **5.** 200, **6.** 89.

PENSA **– Page 10.2**

1. T. T as in TEN. One, Two, Three, Four, Five, Six, Seven, Eight, Nine.

2. 232. Subtract the left-hand side from the right-hand side, double that answer.

3. 14. (Add numbers outside brackets, divide by 50 to get inside number.)

4. Y. A, D, G – 2 steps between, G, K, O – 3 steps between, E, J, ? – 4 steps.

5. O. Similar to #5.

6. 19. (There are 2 alternating series: one goes up by 5; the other goes up by 4)

7. Comforter. All the rest are fish. Pike, Herring, Shark.

8. Harold. The rest are girls' names: Irma, Brigitte, Connie.

9. TOIL. (The 1st letter of the word in brackets is the 2nd letter of the second word, the second is the third letter of the second word, the third is the third letter of the first word, the fourth is the fifth letter of the first word.)

10. **BARS.** (The 1st letter of the word in brackets is the 1st letter of the first word, the second is the third letter of the first word, the third is the second letter of the second word, the fourth is the fifth letter of the second word.)

11. **Pi.** The magic number for Pi (π) – 3.141592654. . . . n–1

12. **20.** Note that the difference between top and bottom numbers always is a prime number. IN this instance he prime is 3.

13. **3.** Notice that if you add up each column, left to right, each sum increases by one, the last column, x = 3, and that column's sum is 16.

14. **14 16.** 144 ÷ 36 = 4; 125 ÷ 25 = 5; 96 ÷ 16 = 6; 126 ÷ 18 = 7; 112 ÷ 8 = 14; 144 ÷ 9 = 16. Incremental order 4, 5, 6, 7, 8, 9.

15. **1543.** All the other years add to 17.

16. **x = 15, y = H, z = 8.** The word "F O U R T **H**", each letter is counted from A as 1, B as 2, etc., **H = 8**; and a second series, 3, 6, 9, 12, **15** is at work.

17. **343.** – Multiply each number by the preceding number and divide by two.

18. **34.** Hard way: The squares of these numbers differs by 1 from the product of the numbers to left and right of them. 21^2 = 441, 13 x 34 = 442.
    Easy way: All numbers formed by adding the immediate left number to form the next in line, 2 + 1 = 3 + 2 = 5 + 3 = 8, etc.,. . . 13 + 21 = 34, . . .

19. **289.** Other numbers are all squares + 12.

20. **face.** a = 1, b = 2, c = 3, etc.

21. **664.** Number in brackets is four times the difference of numbers outside bracket.

22. **63.** As 24 ÷ 8 = 3 x 7 = 21; 35 ÷ 7 = 5 x (7 + 1) 8 = 40; then 56 ÷ 8 = 7 x (8 + 1) 9 = 63

23. **60.** First column divided into 2nd column.That difference is subtracted from 2nd col. number to give answer in 3rd column. 63 ÷ 21 = 3 from 63 = 60.

24. **137.** Twice no. (6 x 2 = 12) + 2 = 14, increase by 2x+2, 2x+3, 2x+4, etc.

25. **139.** Double no. + 1; double next –1; alternate 69 x 2 = 139 + 1 = 139.

26. **a)** 58.

27. **4.** Column 1 x col. 2 divided by col. 4. 9 x 8 ÷28 = 4.

28. 0. Calculate the right answer by doing brackets first, if any. If you have to multiply/divide and add/subtract, do the multiplication/division first.

29. Z. Two series here, skipping 2 and 3 alternately.

30. GLAD. 1st letter left word, 2nd letter right word, 4th letter left, 5th letter right.

31. b) 80.

32. 15. 1st number plus two times 2nd equals 3rd.

33. b) 4/27.

34. 586. Double 1st, plus 2, double 2nd, less 3, double 3rd, plus 4, double 4th, less 5, double 5th, plus 6, etc.

35. e) 64.

36. b) $6\sqrt{5}$.

37. 1456. 1st column is cubed to make 4th column, which is then divided by 4. Of course, the 1st col. number times the 2nd column number gives answer.

38. ans. 4.

39. ans. x = 2.

40. ans. 111. The number inside bracket is 1/2 difference of outside numbers.

Get yourself to Mensa: **MENSA CANADA,**
Box 1025, Station "O",
Toronto, Ontario, Canada
M4A 2N4 (Check for newest phone number)

Exercise 12 – Page 16.10
1. 145, **2.** 189, **3.** 212, **4.** 126, **5.** 188,
6. 199, **7.** 143, **8.** 201, **9.** 187, **10.** 94 (tried to fool you, but it didn't work! – $94^2 \times 2^2 (2 \times 2) = 35344$!)

Exercise 13 – Page 16.10
1. 473, **2.** 586, **3.** 456, **4.** 981, **5.** 589,
6. 728, **7.** 529, **8.** 864, **9.** 862, **10.** 998

Exercise 14 – Page 18.7
1. 17,075,984, **2.** 4,213,946,958 **3.** 22,518 **4.** 148,824 **5.** 562,224,484
6. 25,550,986 **7.** 4,591,145 **8.** 22,694,000 **9.** 12,733,432
10. 3,808,368,746 **11.** 22,808,628 **12.** 43,270,084

Exercise A – Page 19.2
1. 5,476, **4.** 4,096 **7.** 15,376 **10.** 34,596 **13.** 2,319,529
2. 8,649 **5.** 1,444 **8.** 21,316 **11.** 1,481,089 **14.** 3,334,226
3. 6,724 **6.** 12,544 **9.** 28,224 **12.** 2,458,624 **15.** 3,682,561

Exercise B – Page 19.2
1. 33,005 **4.** 76,160 **7.** 22,425
2. 60,261 **5.** 40,716 **8.** 795,615
3. 84,624 **6.** 42,749 **9.** 433,755

Exercise 15 – Page 19.3
1. 32,020,016 **5.** 20,916,024
2. 27,963,179 **6.** 60,174,473
3. 65,608,575 **7.** 66,298,396
4. 21,053,296 **8.** 13,091,247

Exercise 16 (D) – Page 20.1
1. 21,376 **4.** 67,175 **7.** 1,995,056
2. 15,741 **5.** 49,484 **8.** 649,344
3. 5,184 **6.** 61,479 **9.** 533,169

Exercise 17 – Page 20.3
1. 1728 **2.** 216 **3.** 64 **4.** 512 **5.** 1331 **6.** 27 **7.** 729 **8.** 125
9. 8 **10.** 2,197 **11.** 2,744 **12.** 343 **13.** 1,000 **14.** – 1 **15.** 4,096
16. 8,000

Exercise 18 – Page 20.3
1. 204,304 **2.** 50,041,476 **3.** 454,276 **4.** 4,3327,271,524 **5.** 558,009
6. 86,436 **7.** 976,144 **8.** 27,556 **9.** 83,521 **10.** 3,418,801 **11.** 174,724
12. 446,224 **13.** 37,970,244 **14.** 4,604,029,609 **15.** 998,001

Exercise 19 – Page 21.6
1. 473,344 **2.** 432,348,849 **3.** 454,276 **4.** 4,327,271,524 **5.** 558,009
6. 86,436 **7.** 976,144 **8.** 27,556 **9.** 83,521 **10.** 3,418,801 **11.** 174,724
12. 446,224

Exercise 20 – Page 21.6
1. 71,824 **2.** 31,798,321 **3.** 315,844 **4.** 3,216,364,369 **5.** 755,161 **6.** 263,169 **7.** 207,936 **8.** 191,844 **9.** 232,324 **10.** 904,401 **11.** 710,649
12. 471,969 **13.** 395,641 **14.** 727,609 **15.** 788,544

Exercise 21– Page 21.6
1. 1,305 **2.** 5,698 **3.** 3,015 **4.** 5,070 **5.** 2,738 **6.** 406 **7.** 6,664
8. 736 **9.** 812 **10.** 3,822 **11.** 1,148 **12.** 3,828 **13.** 5,642 **14.** 73,551
15. 6,633

Exercise 22– Page 23.6
1. 348 **2.** 231 **3.** 316 **4.** 688 **5.** 702 **6.** 238 **7.** 228 **8.** 891
9. 464 **10.** 549 **11.** 3,510 **12.** 6,324 **13.** 1,356 **14.** 31,464 **15.** 23,115
16. 330,525 **17.** 272,252 **18.** 8,616,465

INDEX

A

Abel, vii
Absolon, vii
Adding Tricks. 17.15
Alcuin of York, vii
Alberti, G. A., 17.2
Annenberg, Walter H., American Education philanthropist, IFC
Answers to book, 24.1-24.5

B

Basis of Arithmetic, 2.1
Be A Whiz Kid!, 1.8 – 1.11
Big Spender – #7, 9.1
BOOMERANGS, 5.1
Boomerang Squaring, 6.3
Boomerang, 3 by 3, 5.14
Brain Power, 18.3
Briggs, (1631), *Logarithmall Arithmetike,* 19.5

C

Caesar, Julius, 17.10
Calculus, 13.11, 14.6 - 14.13
Calendar Trick, Wallace Lee, 17.8
Card Trick, Part I, 2.9; Part II, 13.8
Carroll, Lewis, 17.12
Casting Out Nines, 1.6
Check Friends Number Sense, 21.7
Colburn, Zerah
Combining Mental & Written Math, for best results, 21.3
Coming to Terms with Math, 1.1
Computing Mentally, 4.1
Complementary Multiplying, 5.6
Complementary Squaring, 13.1-2
CRAY Computer, 8.1
Crowds, (groups of numbers), 8.2
Cube Roots and Cubes, 18.1
Cube Formula, 20.2
Cube Tables, 20.6
Cubes of Numbers, 20.3

D

Date Magic, 20.4
Date Squares, Edible, that is, 19.7
Division, 12.5
Division, Short Cuts, 2.3, 22.1 –
Drugs, avoiding, 11.2
Dysert, Willis, 17.2

E

Einstein's Uncle Itzak, 16.13
Eratosthenes, Prime Numbers, 8.2
Euclid, 8.3
Euler, Leonhard, i
Extracting Some Fifth Roots, 18.5

F

Fast Squaring, 13.1
Fibonacci.s Trick, Leonardo, 13.9
Formulae, Geometrica appendix
Fractions, 13.3 - 13.7
Fraction Short Cuts!, 13.6 - 13.7
Further Thoughts, (tricks), 17.12
Future Work In Book to Come, 6.3
Fractions, 3.1, 13.3

G

Galileo, i
Gardner, Martin, 17.12
Gauss, Carl Friedrich, i
Gelosia Method (lattice), see Treviso, 1.5
Gerbert, (mathematician), i
Glossary, G1-G14, (back of book)
Golomb, Solomon W. "Einstein", 17.1
Got a Deck of Cards?, 2.8
Gregorian Calendar, 17.10
Griffith, Arthur A., 11.4
Gregory, Pope, xiii, 17.10

H

Handy Method to Multiply, 21.7
Half-Complement Method, 5.12
High-Speed Multiplication, 23.3
Hindu-Arabic, numbers, 1.4
Hipparchus, astronomer, 14.?
Hylles, (mathematician), i
Hundred Short Cuts, 22.1 –> 22.9

I

Interest, Computing, 15.5
Interest for any Rate, 15.6
Interesting Number Groupings, 11.6
International Math Contest, 19.5
Illiteracy, Innumeracy, 3.3
I.Q. Intelligence Quotient, 10.1

L

Lee Calendar Trick, 17.8
Left to Right Subtraction, 9.3
Lenaghan Boomerangs, 5.1
Lenaghan's Law, 5.13
Logarithms, 16.12, 19.3 - 5,

M

Magic Calendar Phenomenon, 11.7
Math Olympiad Contest, Appendix
Magic reckoning, 3.2
Magic Squares, 6.1
Marvelous Griffith, 17.4

Marvelous Number (1089), 12.2
Math of a Hundred Cuts, 22.1 - 22.9
Math Rip-off, 1.8 - 11
Math Wizard's Up Some,
Down Some, 2.4
Mathematical Structure, 6.4
MENSA, 10.1
Mental Computing, 4.1
Miller, Joe, (jokester), 11.3
Milton Berle, 11.3
Mind Boggler, 4.1
Motivation, 7.5
Mr. Power 142,857!, 12.1
Multi-Minded Mental Marvel, 11.2
Multiplying Complements, 1.4

N

Number Sense, iii, iv. 7.3 - 4
Number Problems, v, vi

O

Old Mystic 76923!, 11.6

P

Patter of Little Feats, 11.4
Peculiar Answers, 17.13
PENSA, 10.1
Pi, π, 20.1
Pope Gregory, 17.10
Positive Numbers, 8.1
Preview to Calculus, 13.11
Prime Numbers, 8.1

Q

Quick Counter (multiplication), 19.6
Quick Look, 1.1
Quite Quick Short Cuts, 20.1

R

Random Numbers, 8.2
Rote Method, 3.2
Repetition Number Trick, 2.2

S

Short Cuts, 1.1, 1.2, 1.3
Short Methods of Multiplying, 1.1
Show Time!, 11.4
Sieve of Eratosthenes, 8.3
Small Square Construction, 16.3
Social Numbers, 8.2
Square Number in Your Head,16.10
Square Roots, Finding, 16.5
Squares and Square Roots, 16.1
Squares and Square Tables, 20.7
Stage 1, 5.1
Stage 2, 5.3
Stage 3, 5.5
Stage 4, 5.9
Stage Calculator-in-training,
4.3, 11.4
Stage Calculators "Supreme", 16.11
Strategies, 4.1
Strange Additions, 9.2

T

Trachtenberg, Jakow, math genius,
i, 23.1 - 6
Treviso, Arithmetic, 1.5
Trick Mathematics, 14.4
Tricky Short Cuts, 20.1
Trigonometry, Snap Review, 14.5
Trivia Time, 17.14
Twisty Question?, 16.4

U

Up Some, Down Some, 2.4

W

Wallace, Lee, 17.5
Waring, 12.3
Washington, George, 17.10
Week Teaser!, 18.6
Wessel, vii, mathematician
Willie, the Wizard, 17.1

X

Xerses, vii, mathematician

Z

Zeno of Elea, vii, mathematician

(We invite your response to this book and offer a Membership in the renewed interest in Mathematics from students of all ages. "Seven to Seventy" is no idle statement for having an enquiring mind in the many ways Mathematics and Entertainment can be molded together as a skill.

Please answer the attached Card and mail to the address noted on it. Join in the Can-Am Math Olympiad. It's fun and it's cash rewarding!

Send in your Membership Form, with a self-addressed and a stamped envelope. Get your membership card in as soon as possible. We will send it out within a 2-week time period.

Happy Math Results!

WIN MATH CASH PRIZES!

SUPER MATH-E-MAGICS!!

"CAN-AM MATH COMPETITION

Compete with your own mental age group.

Contest Form included with original purchase. Continental areas will enter series of elimination tests based on the knowledge learned from the SUPER MATH-E-MAGICS Handbook ONLY! Stage Presentation, agility and speed in arriving at correct answers will be totalled and the Grand Prize winner in each area will face off on National TV. *** Prize levels at each and every local contest will have mathematic teachers as final judges. Each area finalist of Continental North America (Canada and the United States) will enter the next up-grade contest until just 10 finalists will match wits, humour, intelligence until the last three best surface for the Television Showdown. Proof of sale for the SUPER MATH-E-MAGICS! book is mandatory. No copies, facsimiles or reproductions allowed. Any attempt at falsification of documents, sales slips, etc., leads to immediate disqualification from contest presence. No Calculator – just a clear mind, a pencil and paper are permitted. "ENTER TODAY!!!

The Semi-Finals for the CAN-AM MATH CONTESTS based on the theories and strategies of "SUPER MATH-E-MAGICS!!" will be held in the the Spring of 1995. The winners will face off in the Continental Playoffs in July, 1995. Winners of the different levels will be informed of their areas of Math problems and printed tests similar to the Finals will be available. We also plan on a PAN-AM MATH CONTEST.

ALGOTEXT PUBLISHING will accept School Teams from Different School Boards wishing to compete in a Math Bee Format. Special Prize Money will be made available. Only Teams in the same age groups.

5% OF EACH BOOK SALE PROFIT WILL ACCUMULATE TO THE MATH AWARD FUND AND WILL BE HELD IN TRUST AT THE BANK OF NOVA SCOTIA IN TORONTO, ONTARIO, CANADA. ENTRANTS WILL BE NOTIFIED IN WRITING OF ALL CONTEST DATES AND AWARD PRIZES MONEY!

Let's find out if you're as good as you think you are!

"Remember, every one is a genius if one is given enough time!"